FIREMAN!

A Personal Account

FIREMAN!

A PERSONAL ACCOUNT

NEIL WALLINGTON

With a Foreword by Gordon Honeycombe

David & Charles
Newton Abbot   London   North Pomfret (Vt)

British Library Cataloguing in Publication Data
Wallington, Neil
Fireman!
1. Fire – departments – England – London
2. London – Fires and fire prevention
I. Title
628.9'25'0924   TH9539.L/
ISBN 0–7153–7723–X

Library of Congress Catalog Card Number 78–65762

First published 1979
Second impression 1980

© Neil Wallington 1979

Printed in Great Britain
by Biddles Limited, Guildford
for David & Charles (Publishers) Limited
Brunel House Newton Abbot Devon

Published in the United States of America
by David & Charles Inc
North Pomfret Vermont 05053 USA

Contents

FOR SUE

Foreword

Not all calls received by a Fire Brigade are fire-calls. In fact, in an average year in London, only about half the total of calls will be to fires – the rest will be false alarms (whether of good intent or malicious) and calls involving 'special services'. Heading this last category by a long way are calls to release a 'person shut in lift'. Then come 'road traffic accidents', followed closely by 'persons locked out'. It was as a locked-out person that I first met Neil Wallington.

At the time he was the Station Officer in charge of the Red Watch at Paddington Fire Station (A21) in London. I had already met most of the Watch through a charity event – in June 1974 the Red Watch had raised £1,500 for the RNLI and the Multiple Sclerosis Society by *rowing* around London, via the river and canals. I was involved in this in a small way, and for the first time learned something about firemen and the vital but generally unappreciated job they did. Several times I rode with them on their machines to shouts (fire-calls), although I never actually saw a fire. I never met their Station Officer as he was away on a lengthy course, and I *never* thought I would one day have to call on them myself for professional assistance.

What happened was that on leaving my second-floor flat in a hurry one lunchtime, I accidentally locked myself out by shutting the flat's front door, with the key on the other side. Rather than summon police help, I telephoned Paddington Fire Station for their advice and for the phone number of

Belsize Fire Station, on whose ground my flat was situated –
each fire station having an area of specific responsibility, their
'ground'. I hoped Belsize might come to my rescue. As it
happened, the Red Watch were on duty that afternoon, and
as it happened Belsize must have been very busy, for my
phone-calls went unanswered. Checking with Paddington later
that I had the right phone-number, the Station Officer told me
not to worry, and to go back to my flat – he and a crew from
Paddington would come to my assistance, unofficially, as my
flat was not on their ground, although on one adjacent to
theirs. Some ten minutes later A21's Pump arrived with a
four-man crew all in fire-gear, an extension ladder was raised
to a window, the catch was slipped, the window was opened,
and a fireman climbed through to open the front door from
the inside.

In gratitude I asked all five inside for a drink – the firemen
had cokes and the Station Officer a scotch. They only stayed a
few minutes, but that was how Neil and I met.

He was, and is, brisk and energetic, tall and spare of build;
afterwards I learned he was a keen cross-country runner, and
an avid reader and collector of books about steam trains. He
was then thirty-two.

I saw him again in September and October when I called in
at Paddington Fire Station to have a drink in their Social Club.
Nothing of any great excitement or importance happened in
the way of shouts when I was there (for which reason alone my
presence was always welcome), but I heard many more stories
and views about the Fire Service – so much, indeed, that was
dramatic, humorous and unknown that I said: 'Why doesn't
someone write about you? Why don't you write something
about yourselves?' But I never dreamed that one day I, and
now Neil, would do just that.

Then two months later, in the early hours of Friday, 13
December 1974, the Red Watch were called out to deal with
the worst fire in central London that year, a 30 pump fire at
the Worsley Hotel, Maida Vale. Twenty-four people were
rescued, but seven people died in the fire, including a fireman.

He and three other firemen, who were seriously injured, were buried by debris in a small second-floor room when the roof and the third floor collapsed on top of them. Two of them, and the dead fireman, came from Neil Wallington's Watch. He himself, as the Station Officer in charge of the first four machines to reach the fire, which was on their ground, was heavily involved in fire-fighting operations and in the rescue of the buried firemen. Strangely, he had only left the room in which they were buried seconds before the collapse.

The following year he was one of twenty-two firemen given awards by the Greater London Council for the bravery, initiative, skill and perseverance they had displayed at the Worsley Hotel fire, and one of the eight who were honoured later by the Queen, he himself receiving the Queen's Commendation for Brave Conduct.

The fatal fire at the Worsley Hotel was fatal in more than one way, and extraordinary in many, the deaths and rescues of civilians being compounded by the death and rescue of firemen. Visiting the Fire Station after Christmas I heard the inside story of what had actually happened at the fire from the men most directly involved. Their accounts deeply impressed me and brought into focus all I had heard before and thought and learned about the Fire Service. Here was a story worth telling, and it had never been told before.

However, the resulting book, *Red Watch*, could never have been written without the sustained and whole-hearted co-operation of the Red Watch, and in particular of their Station Officer, Neil Wallington. As it happened, he was also something of a writer, having penned several articles for the London Fire Brigade's magazine, *London Fireman*. He was thus more aware than most firemen of the difficulties of my task, and eager to assist in making the book as authentic as possible. His help and sympathy were invaluable.

It is therefore a particular pleasure for me to welcome *his* book and to introduce it to you – a fireman's own account of the selfless public service afforded by firemen everywhere, a service too often taken for granted, and exceptional in that firemen, knowingly and actually, put their own lives at risk in saving the lives and property of others.

This book, the first of its kind to be published, apart from being truly informative, humorous and dramatic, pays a long-overdue tribute to the work of firemen throughout the country, to the men who watch and wait for twenty-four hours of every day, of every month, of every year, ready to deal with the unknown dangers that accident, malice and envy can bring to others, and to themselves.

Gordon Honeycombe
Bournemouth, August 1978

Introduction

When a brave policeman or passer-by attempts to defy the flames and dense smoke of a burning house to rescue a trapped woman and child, the newspapers will probably be full of their heroic efforts, even if they are unsuccessful. When the Fire Brigade arrives and enters the blazing building and effects a rescue, the media will say little if anything about it. The firemen, after all, are only doing their job – what is expected of them. As the limp forms of a mother and child are carried out of the gutted rooms by firemen and rushed away by ambulance, few will appreciate the sweat, toil, self-discipline and courage which have been displayed inside the burning house. Out of sight is out of mind. On the rare occasions when firemen *are* shown on the television news they appear to be largely inactive, silhouetted against the flames, wandering about or merely projecting powerful jets of water into the inferno. But this is nothing like a true portrayal of a fireman's work.

Sir Eyre Massey Shaw, who from 1861 to 1891 commanded the Metropolitan Fire Brigade (which became the London Fire Brigade in 1903), and was the father of modern fire-fighting techniques, said:

A fireman, to be successful, must enter buildings. He must get in below, above, on every side; from opposite houses, over back walls, over side walls, through panels of doors, through windows, through skylights, through holes cut by himself in gates, walls and the roof. He must know how to reach the attic from the basement by ladders placed on half-

11

burned stairs, and the basement from the attic by a rope made fast on a chimney. His whole success depends on his getting in and remaining there, and he must always carry his appliances with him, as without them he is of no use.

Massey Shaw's edict laid down the fundamentals of professional fire-fighting, and his words are as apposite today as when written over a hundred years ago. But as the majority of fires are fought from *within* a building, a cameraman or observer cannot easily follow firemen into their working environment. If they could, they would discover the severe physical conditions in which firemen labour, even in bringing a small fire under control. Intense heat that toasts faces, ears and backs of necks, and dense choking smoke; all these are a fireman's mortal enemy.

A 1971 government inquiry into the work of the Fire Service concluded:

A fireman must have special personal qualities. He must have physical courage. On occasions he must voluntarily face extremities of danger which confront few other people in time of peace. It is the element of risk and the demand for courage which sets a fireman's job apart from others. But bravery is not the only personal quality needed. A fireman must be able to work as part of a closely integrated team, the watch to which he belongs. He must be prepared to obey orders without question, especially on the fire-ground. At the same time he must be able to show initiative when working on his own. All of these qualities may be needed in other occupations; but we know of none in which, together with courage in the face of danger, they are needed in combination to such a degree as in the fire service.

Picture a typical fire scene in London – a tenement block of seedy dwellings. Black smoke is pouring ominously from a first-floor window as the first Brigade appliances (fire-engines) arrive. Quickly it is established that there is nobody still in the building and that no life needs to be saved. It looks like a routine job. Several firemen, already wearing their cumbersome breathing-apparatus sets, try to get up a staircase which is already choked with thick smoke. They manhandle a charged hose-line up the stairs, dragging it with them, a lifeline to their five supporting colleagues below and the appliances outside. With pulses racing, the leading team of firemen gain the landing. The heat is ever-increasing and they feel as if they are in an oven, but no water jet is let off until the fire is found, except for an occasional fine spray to cool their scorching faces as they force themselves on through the heat and darkness.

Suddenly, through the smoke, their quarry is seen – an orange fire-glow eating away at the bottom edge of a door ahead. The fireman controlling the nozzle turns on the jet of water just before the second fire-fighter kicks open the door and the unleashed column of water knocks back the first rampant charge of the flames onto the landing, leaping out and right over the heads of the firemen now lying prone on the floor. They are lost in a whirlwind of superheated steam, flying burning embers and smoke, but they hold their ground. Part of the ceiling above breaks away and falls, showering them with hot plaster. Slowly, working as a team, and with other firemen straightening and easing the heavy hose behind them, the leading crew advance into the burning room and the swirling vortex of steam and smoke, their jet of water hissing as they rotate it systematically in front of them.

Five minutes later, the blaze in the house is out, and although small pockets of fire still linger under the debris, the atmosphere has cleared sufficiently for the damage to be surveyed. One room and its contents are burnt out, plaster has spalled off the walls, and the timber skirting-boards, window and door-frames are charred and blackened. Someone's home and treasured possessions are irretrievably ruined. The Station Officer in charge of the firemen now has time to seek out the occupier of the premises, to break the news relating to the damage in the room, and to try to establish the cause of the outbreak. In doing so, he makes use of some of the lessons in psychology which his profession has taught him, lending a sympathetic ear and, occasionally, a shoulder to cry on. Several crews of sweaty, grimy firemen emerge from the tenement for a brief respite, gulping the cold clean air, and remove their breathing-apparatus sets, shake off some of the dust and cool their burning faces and necks. By their efforts, the fire has been contained to one room, although there is considerable heat and smoke damage to the rest of the tenement. However, this time there has been no need for any spectacular or hazardous rescue by the first firemen on the scene, and no disfigured and charred body remains to be wrapped up and carried down to a waiting ambulance.

At this back-street scene there is no newspaper reporter, just a solitary PC keeping back a small crowd of onlookers, who begin to drift away when they realise that all the visible action is over. For the firemen now clearing up, this was a 'good' fire. 'Good' in that it was contained before it really took hold, for although inwardly most firemen enjoy the spectacle of a major blaze, they certainly do not relish the effort that will be needed to control it.

In addition to fire-calls, firemen today are increasingly summoned to all kinds of other incidents. These are termed 'special services' and increase in number and variety each year, ranging from dealing with the extreme hazards of lethal chemicals leaking from road tankers, or the extrication of people trapped in road and railway accidents, to such mundane tasks as releasing people shut in a lift stuck between floors in a tower block. A Fire Brigade has the resources and the skilled men to cope with such incidents and it is at 'special service' calls that the public get a clearer view of firemen at work.

Emergency calls, however, only account for a small part of a fireman's hours on duty. He must be in a state of constant readiness, along with all his equipment, and regular re-training and drills thus occupy much of his time between emergency calls. A fireman must check, maintain and be familiar with the hundred-and-one items carried in the lockers on the appliances, including his own life-support system (his breathing-apparatus set). He will also be involved in fire-prevention safety checks and inspections of certain buildings, as required by law. All the accounts of fires and other incidents in this book concern true events and, because the very nature of a fireman's work demands and develops a strong sense of humour, many of the accounts are light-hearted. The more serious side of the work, with its dangers, fatalities and moments of sheer horror, can be imagined; they are often too grim and grisly to relate.

I have tried to portray something of the life of a fireman through my experiences and those of other firemen – a world that normally lies hidden behind the closed doors of a fire station until suddenly they crash open and one or two bright-red appliances emerge, with blue warning-beacons flashing and two-tone horns sounding, heading off on yet another mercy mission.

1

The First Fire

The two-tone horns blared into the settling dusk and the fire-bell clanged an urgent warning to the scattering traffic as the fire-engine heeled into the roundabout and then swung up the rise into Purley Way. Hanging out of a side window, I peered out from under my fire-helmet towards our destination. As I focused on the outline of the industrial estate ahead, the cold night air rushed past and suddenly I trembled with excitement. There hanging low over the huddled factories and warehouses was a deep-red flickering glow.

Over the din of the horns and bell, the Sub-Officer in charge of the appliance called out: 'We've got a bloody good job here. In the roof by the look of things.' He could see far more from his front seat than the crew in the rear cab and both Mick, the experienced fireman alongside me, and I leant right out of each side window to get another view of the blaze awaiting us. As the appliance raced up the outside of a line of halted traffic whose drivers waved us urgently past, the angry glow over the buildings ahead had intensified and once again I felt a tremble run through me.

The first of several 999 fire-calls to Bowater's paper store had been received at Croydon fire station at 9pm and all five fire appliances from the station had turned out in response. Bowater's occupied an old aircraft hanger on the Croydon Aerodrome site and it was usually full of paper products. Now, only three minutes after the first 999 call, our appliance, the first of the convoy of Croydon fire-fighters, swung off Purley Way and into Bowater's entrance. The powerful headlight beams picked

17

out wafting traces of dark smoke, and high over a roof leaping flames were now clearly visible, licking skyward. This was my first sight of a major fire for I had only been an operational fireman for a few weeks since passing out from training school.

A uniformed security guard ran towards our appliance and flagged it down. 'Quick – it's No 2 paper-reel warehouse! Follow the road around to the back and the main doors are on the left.'

The driver moved the appliance hard off through the lower gears. The headlights behind us showed that the other Croydon appliances were now in close support. All around, the smoke grew thicker. Then quite suddenly as the fire appliance drew upwind of the fire, the smoke cleared and there was the open yard in front of the burning warehouse. Our appliance screeched to a halt on the loose gravel, the doors flew open and Mick and I piled out. The Sub-Officer ran to assess the fire situation, shouting out: 'Two jets, fast as you can, and Wallington, get the Pump Escape [our appliance] set into a hydrant – the nearest one's back down the road.'

Above, fire was breaking through all along the ridge and eaves of the large single-storey warehouse, some 150 feet in length, which bordered the yard. Showers of orange sparks rose angrily into the night sky and in the distance I could hear more two-tone horns and fire-bells as reinforcements approached from other fire stations.

All the other fire appliances from Croydon had pulled up nearby and were disgorging their crews. My pulse was racing as I grabbed a standpipe, key and bar from a locker and set off at the double. I had only taken a few strides when, clumsily anxious, I cannoned into another fireman as he came running out of the smoke towards me. 'Sorry Mick,' and I set off again in search of a hydrant. Mick had been one of the first firemen to befriend me when I arrived at Croydon Fire Station.

(*Opposite*)
A major fire at its height as a Thameside warehouse blazes – St Katherine's Dock, November 1973. Note the partially collapsed outer wall on the right (*Owen Rowland*)

Once I had found the hydrant and run out hose to connect to the appliance, it was clear even to my raw eye that this fire was going to take a lot of effort and skill to contain and extinguish. The flames along the roof seemed to get stronger every minute and from within the doomed warehouse came a constant roar as they took a fiercer hold. My muscles still trembled with excitement as the drama of the scene unfolded, firemen dashing around everywhere. After my initial task with the hydrant, I rejoined the rest of my crew who were very close to the fire itself and playing two jets of water into the leaping flames of the warehouse only 40 feet away. Wave after wave of searing heat rippled over me and the others of the crew. I took up position to support a fireman as he struggled to control a heavy and reactive jet of water, and attempted to aim the stream into the fire through a high window in the warehouse. In the light of the flames I saw it was Mick and, as I brought my weight to bear on the pulsating and snake-like hose right behind him he cried: 'Keep your bloody head down. The roof's already gone here and soon there'll be precious little to hold the structure together. The place is full of large paper reels.'

Mick had already turned his fire-helmet around back-to-front so that the neck curtain gave more protection against the blistering heat and I did the same. Frighteningly, the radiated heat that Mick and I faced along with all the other fire-fighters on the long frontage of the warehouse was so intense that timber door and window frames of a building remote across the yard were smouldering. To protect and cool these, several jets of water were aimed at all the fronts of buildings at risk.

The warehouse fire was now surrounded by jets of water on all sides but despite this, from my position at one side of the roaring blaze, I was transfixed by the sheer devastation and ferocious energy of the inferno. In addition to the long-reaching jet, Mick had turned on the fine-spray control of the nozzle, which provided a water-mist curtain behind which we could find a little respite from the roasting heat as he and I tried to advance towards the warehouse foot by foot. In the fearsome

The hazard of falling walls: a fire in an empty warehouse in
Wapping, East London, March 1976 (*LFB*)

heat, the very outer edges of the spray turned magically into
wisps of steam and were quickly drawn off into the night.

From within the warehouse, large burning fragments of
paper took off in the upward draught of the fire and rose to
join a stream of smaller glowing sparks. Every property down-
wind of the fire was at risk from the flying brands and the
Assistant Chief Officer, Mr Lloyd, now in command of the
fire-fighting operations, had positioned some crews with hose-
lines on nearby roofs to cover this danger.

As I crouched behind Mick on our jet, I heard him swear
violently several times as, section by section, the warehouse
roof collapsed into the fire, sending yet more showers of
brilliant sparks burgeoning into the sky. Bricks and roofing
panels crashed down and landed around us, many of the
bricks being so hot that they sizzled in the bitumen surfacing
of the yard. The flickering light from the fire illuminated the
entire area with a bright orange tint, and Mick and I were
reluctantly forced to retreat.

After several minutes, I noticed part of the large metal sliding door of the warehouse directly in front of us was glowing red-hot. With most of the roof now fallen in, the hundreds of paper reels inside provided a constant fuel for the hungry and consuming fire – 'Watch that bastard door!' Flames leapt even higher up over the warehouse and hundreds of fiery fragments fell around us like confetti. Several settled upon my fire-tunic and burnt holes before I realised and knocked them off. Suddenly, and as if in slow-motion, the large sliding door in front of us started to fall outwards; it hit the ground with a resounding clang. Long tongues of pointed flame blew out of the inferno towards our position. Mick pulled me down to the ground unceremoniously, yet we still clung to our jet which was aimed deep into the swirling red interior now visible through the gaping hole where the door had stood. Flames rippled and rolled unchecked over the stacked paper reels inside as the fearful heat swept over us. Then, just as Mick and I resumed our crouched stances, part of the end wall fell into the interior onto the stacked reels and two of these came rolling out of the warehouse towards us, like giant burning Catherine wheels. Mick and I were able to repel these with the powerful pressure of our jet and they rocked to a halt, still flaming at the edges only feet from us.

About a hundred firemen with twenty appliances were at work, but the fire slowly engulfed the warehouse. The building sagged and fell apart, piece by piece as if in its death throes.

Along with the rest of my crew, I left the scene of Bowater's fire some hours later, in the early hours of the morning, when we were relieved by a fresh crew from another fire station. By this time, the warehouse was reduced to a crumbling, twisted, smoking shell. My first major fire had been a battle lost.

I was tired, wet through to the skin and my limbs ached. My uniform reeked of smoke and even in the clear cool air away from the devastated scene all I could smell was the aroma of fire. My eyes were sore and my face was reddened and tingled from its exposure to the awful heat. For the first time since I joined the Fire Brigade, I felt like a real fireman.

2
Raw Recruit

The Recruit on the Drill Tower

All right for him to shout at me,
I'm shaking like an Aspen leaf.
He's on the ground, I'm three floors up.
It's me not he will come to grief.

Charles Clisby

What makes a man want to be a fireman? Possibly, as in my case, the soul-destroying humdrum nature of a nine-to-five job; perhaps the prospect of excitement, the certain glamour of being a fire-fighter, the predominantly outdoor life and the desire to work with a close-knit body of men.

Today, the security and pay may be attractions also. At the time of writing, an eighteen-year-old newly joined fireman in the London Fire Brigade earns over £3,500 per annum from the time he is posted to training school. However, when I joined the County Borough of Croydon Brigade in 1964 at the age of twenty-two, the annual pay was around £830, which was well below the industrial average of that time. A fireman's working week then, as now, was also longer than the national average. The Croydon Brigade was one of the first to attain a 56 hour week. The Greater London Fire Brigade, which absorbed the Croydon Brigade in 1965, went over to a 48 hour week in November 1974 and has still not achieved national parity in this respect.

When I joined, it was an accepted part of a fireman's duties to clean his own fire station until it shone like a new pin. I well remember my first interview when the interviewing officer asked me why I wanted to be a fireman. Nervously I explained my wish to work outdoors, see some excitement and be in a job where I could help my fellow men. 'Have you ever cleaned lavatory pans before?' And to my rather puzzled 'Why, no, sir', the officer explained that, if I was successful in joining his Brigade, after basic training part of each day would be spent in certain domestic cleaning tasks around the fire station including all the toilets which, in that size of station, amounted to quite a few. 'Could I cope?' Straight-faced I replied that of course I could.

And I meant it. Little did I realise though just what he meant by 'domestic cleaning'. In fact, after my eleven-week recruit's training course at the London Fire Brigade Training School at Southwark, I was posted to that very headquarters fire station in Old Town, Croydon, where that first interview took place. Here I spent many wearying hours in between emergency calls, longing for the call bells to go off more often, working with both hand and electric polishers on what seemed like acres of floors and corridors which were gleaming even before I started on them. About this time a large proportion of firemen were ex-National Servicemen, and such mundane chores did not seem to worry them unduly. Perhaps this was because they knew the secrets of successful skiving and how to get the easiest jobs while I always seemed to end up with the heavy polisher and the WCs. Since the late sixties however, through the pressure of the firemen's union, all station cleaning has been done by civilian contractors, thereby releasing firemen for additional training and drills and involving them more in fire-prevention and safety work.

An applicant for the Fire Brigade today must be aged between 18 and 30 (34 in the case of ex-servicemen), have a minimum height of 5ft 6in, a chest measurement of 36in – with a minimum expansion of 2in – and not need to wear glasses. After a basic interview, educational examination and a rigorous medical, a successful applicant is sent to the Brigade

Hook-ladder drill at second-floor level of a fire station drill tower. The man is attached to the lower ladder only by the hook of his belt, and fine control and balance are required. He will continue (with another fireman, out of view) with the two ladders to the seventh floor (*LFB*)

training school at Southwark for the eleven-week course.

This basic training gives a recruit an insight into the theory of fire-fighting, although the emphasis is understandably on the practical aspect. At Southwark over the weeks, raw recruits are shaped and moulded into firemen. The instructors unravel the many mysteries of hose, pumps and primers, knots and lines, sprinkler systems, foam equipment, extinguishers and a host of other fire-fighting subjects. A recruit forms part of a squad of trainees who learn to manhandle a London fireman's basic rescue ladder – the three-quarter-ton wheeled escape. At rescue situations, this ladder is quickly pulled off its carrying appliance and wound up manually as required to its maximum working height of 50 feet. Recruits also learn to use the 35-foot general-purpose extension ladder in drill situations.

Then after a first week on these ladders, a recruit looks up to the upper floors of the drill tower with a mixture of fear and awe, at other more advanced squads using hook-ladders high up above the drill yard.

A hook-ladder is made of ash, 13 feet long and only 10 inches wide, weighing only 35 pounds. At its top it has a metal hook with serrated teeth on the underside. This ladder is normally used in a vertical position with the hook put through a window or over a sill – the ladder thus hangs suspended. A fireman then climbs up to the next floor, pulls the ladder up and pitches it to the floor above and so on. In this manner, the face of a building can be scaled quite irrespective of parked cars and other obstacles blocking a wheeled escape. Many brigades in the UK are phasing out the hook-ladder, yet in the London Brigade, as well as being a basic training item, firemen still use them for rescues. In some extreme cases, rescued persons are themselves guided down hook-ladders to safety below.

Like the rest of my fellow recruits I was scared stiff when our instructor, Sub-Officer Groves, assembled all fifteen of us around the base of the six-floor drill tower ready for our first lesson in hook-ladders. Bill Groves was a thickset Londoner, a fire officer of considerable experience, less inclined to shout and bawl at his charges than most of the other instructors. First, he demonstrated how the ladder was lifted into the vertical position and how the long hook at the top was placed into the sill of the first-floor window. He then climbed up and down to the first floor several times showing how easy it was, providing the left hand and left foot, then right hand and right foot, moved in synchronised time. One by one, we tried the fearsome ladder up to the first floor, it did not seem too bad after all. 'Wait till you go higher – it's terrible,' said one tenth-week recruit to me after this first encounter.

And terrible it was. One cold and windy morning of the second week of the course came the session when the Sub-Officer coaxed us all, turn by turn, to sit in at the first-floor window, then lift the single hook-ladder out and gingerly raise it 6 inches at a time to hook into the next window above. This was no easy feat with a strong wind blowing and arm muscles shaking as they tried to control the ladder above. When my turn came, I pitched the ladder up, then grasped the bottom of it and climbed out, trembling and fearful to look down. As I ascended to the second floor up the vertical climb, the hook-ladder seemed to vibrate throughout its flimsy length. When my eyes came level with the sill of the window and I saw only two of the serrated teeth biting into the timberwork and suspending me 40 feet above the ground, I thought 'I'll never make it any higher.' Others in the squad apparently felt the same, but over several following sessions, a little confidence emerged. 'Come on man, up you go, left hand and foot together. Keep going. That's it. Up and in you go!' Every time I swung my leg into the safety and security of the drill-tower levels I was sweating profusely, arms aching from pushing the hook-ladder up and heart pounding.

From this stage the squad slowly progressed to the full two-man, two-ladder drill, in which the fireman on the upper ladder is suspended from a metal ring on his ladder by a safety belt; this leaves his hands free to take hold of the lower ladder when it is passed up to him.

At this point however, one of the squad met with real difficulty. Keith was probably the quietest member of our group, a ginger-haired serious-looking lad of twenty-one. He had had some problems earlier coming to terms with hook-ladder work, especially when Sub-Officer Groves took us above the second floor for the first time. On this morning, Keith froze at this level, unable to command his mind and body to climb out and go up higher. Rather than shout at Keith from the ground, Bill Groves dismissed the rest of the squad for ten minutes for a breather, went up the tower and sat alongside Keith, then went up and down several times himself. He then held the bottom of Keith's hook-ladder as the reluctant recruit struggled out into the position ready to climb up. I watched this scene from a window of an equipment store below and saw Keith's demon slowly being exorcised. By the end of the week, Keith

27

had conquered his fear of heights and my respect for our instructor grew.

Whilst at training school, recruits learn the physics and chemistry of fire extinction, of pressure and vacuum, and the other associated science of getting vast quantities of water from one point to another. They are taught the procedures in force both on a fire station and at emergency calls, and they hear something of the history and tradition of the Brigade.

There is also a new language of expressions to learn. For many years in Victorian times, because of the duty system which demanded that firemen live on a station and be on call twenty-four hours a day, and the physical strength and discipline needed to work at heights, the Brigade only recruited ex-seamen and with them came some of their terminology. Hence going up a ladder is 'going aloft', a hose hauled up the face of a building is 'hauled aloft', anything not secured properly is said to have 'come adrift'. Fire stations are even referred to as 'ships'.

At Southwark, an instructor also teaches his squad the beginnings of the considerable subject of 'firemanship' – applying the basic skills and techniques of fire-fighting to any given situation. A fireman builds upon this teaching the very day he passes out in his training-school parade and is posted to one of London's 114 fire stations to begin his newly chosen profession.

By this time, some of his fellow recruits have possibly fallen by the wayside. The heights, hook-ladder drill or the physical duress of the course take their toll. Looking back on my time at Southwark, there were hardly any of my squad who did not have some phobia in the early stages of the course and, like Bill Groves, many of the other instructors worked hard to overcome these difficulties.

It is at training school, too, that one first meets the camaraderie of Fire Service life. Every instructor seemed to know all there was to know about 'Fire Brigade-ology', worked us like beavers, coaxed and coerced the slower members of the squad, would make a coarse comment that split our sides laughing, yet could still bite your backside off at twenty paces when you made a hash of a drill. On one occasion, four of the squad, including myself, had just started to perform an extension-ladder drill in the midst of a downpour. This first involved pulling the ladder off the roof of the appliance, each of us supporting a corner as the ladder slid off. All this was, of course, done at the double. In our dash, my grip on the ladder sides slipped just as I took my share of the weight and as we started running towards the drill tower with the ladder horizontally between us, my corner fell from my grasp and the ladder edge grated noisily across the surface of the drill yard. 'Don't damage that bloody ladder! Don't you *dare* damage that ladder!' bellowed Sub-Officer Groves. It was one of the few times that I saw him really cross and I recall running around at drill even faster for the rest of that rainy morning. I never dropped a ladder again. Eleven weeks at Southwark was a real education and prelude to what was to come.

Being a disciplined and uniformed body, the Fire Brigade has certain standards and it is probably at training school that these are most rigidly enforced. I especially remember the mass haircuts during the first day of training, when I along with the rest of my squad were inspected by a fearsome Assistant Divisional Officer with a voice straight off the Guards' parade ground. He despatched most of us around the corner to a barber's shop for a short-back-and-sides. No wonder the barber smiled as we all trooped through his door, long-faced and wondering if we would survive another ten weeks like this one. He must have made a small fortune out of recruit firemen over the years.

My basic training took place during winter, in snow, ice and rain. Despite this, the many varied outside drills were still done at the double and after such a session there was always a hectic rush to change out of a dripping-wet fire tunic, grab a hot shower and scramble into the next classroom lesson. Amongst the particular delights first thing in the morning after a full parade and roll-call was the anticipation of your group being nominated for squad drill or PT: you either loved or loathed these activities, whether ex-serviceman or not.

'What use is squad drill to a fireman anyway?' was the inevitable question. 'To teach a quick reaction to a word of command and to move a body of men from A to B in an orderly manner,' came the equally inevitable reply. 'Why not use a mini-bus?' retorted Nobby Clarke, a Cockney colleague who always argued. Indeed, there were those of the squad who had two left feet and never seemed able to anticipate or execute a word of command, to the frequent frustration of the squad drill instructor, Sub-Officer Thomas. He would shout and fume and at times looked as if he would burst with rage: squad drill could be entertaining, providing you were able to conceal your mirth.

Being stripped to the waist for PT at 8.30am on a cold and frosty morning left me breathless, but I grew to enjoy the exercise, the teamwork and the spirit which was gradually developing, and the warm inner glow when the exercises were over. Nobby, of course, complained bitterly. The physical pace of the recruits' course never let up, for PT was usually followed by a 2-hour stint of escape-ladder and pump drill, quite enough to keep the blood coursing through the veins.

Towards the end of my recruit's course came a baptism in smoke. To create a smoke situation an exercise in the basement part of the training school was planned. This section of the building consisted of a number of specially constructed interconnecting rooms, crawling galleries and search areas normally used by qualified firemen undergoing breathing-apparatus training. For recruits this was a much-feared day, for we had all heard tales of the 'rat-run'.

Our instructor first lit a smouldering fire of rags and wood chips in a brazier and allowed it to burn for ten minutes or so. Following a briefing, we entered the basement stairs and headed down into the smoke from where we had to find our way out to an alternative exit and the outside world. I don't think any of the squad realised just how awful those few minutes would be. We scrambled and groped our way through the thick rolling murk and got down on our tummies, as we had been taught, in order to seek what little precious oxygen was trapped at floor level. Our eyes streamed, our hearts pounded and we coughed and spluttered until our lungs felt as if they would be torn out of our chests. After what seemed an eternity, our group broke thankfully out through the exit into the cool clean air of the drill yard.

Some of the squad suffered more than others – one fellow even gave up smoking there and then. We all thought that we had qualified as 'smoke-eaters': little did we realise that this brief encounter was only a taste of what a fireman has to contend with in his normal operational work. Today, a breathing apparatus set is at the disposal of virtually every fireman in London Brigade, to make his task safer and more comfortable. Quite often, even the smoke *outside* a burning building can be so thick that a BA set is needed. Smoke never loses its dark threat to a fire-fighter, and once I was operational I was soon to find out that smoke, not fire, is the real killer.

Another outstanding session at training school, towards the conclusion of the course, was a ride at the head of a turntable ladder. TLs, as they are known, are massive appliances with mechanically operated four-piece metal ladder sections that extend to 100 feet and can rotate through a complete circle. I climbed up onto the 6-inch-wide platform at the top, hooked on my safety belt and gave the ladder operator the 'ready' signal. I was then projected up at an angle of some 70° to 100 feet very quickly; a sensation not unlike being in a very fast lift. I clung to the sides of the ladder and tried hard not to look down at the drill yard that was receding below at an alarming rate. Having attained the maximum extension of the TL, the operator below then proceeded to put the ladder through various evolutions for my benefit. These included reducing the angle of the ladder until it was almost parallel with the ground; then he elevated it again and turned the ladder about its axis, through a complete circle. As each particular movement ceased, there I was at the top of a gently swaying TL, 100 feet up and totally remote from any sensation of noise, except for the operator's occasional enquiry over the intercom system – 'You all right up there?' I mumbled back down to him that I was, although I felt too sick to enjoy the splendid view of central London.

Subsequently, I served at several TL fire stations in London and over the years have had my share of excitement when silhouetted against the flames of burning buildings, as the ladder nozzle poured water into the blaze below. Although I also qualified as both TL driver and operator in later years, I never forgot that very first TL 'ride' at Southwark.

Very quickly it seemed that the final examinations were upon my squad, and with the written part finished, we took to the drill yard to display our expertise with ladders and hose. The hook-ladder drill was done as a two-man exercise using two ladders. When my turn came, all went well until I was seated in at the third-floor window-sill of the tower. My colleague in this drill, Ron Bentley, had reached the fourth-floor level above my head, hooked his safety-belt onto the top hook-ladder and prepared to take hold of the ladder that I was ready to pass up to him. As he heaved my ladder up, its lowest rung lodged neatly into the spring hook of the safety belt around my waist! Ron above failed to feel the resistance and added weight of my eleven stones, pulled up hard on the ladder and almost unseated me from the window position. We finally sorted ourselves out and pressed on up to the top of the tower, six floors up, both thinking 'That's our lot.' Somewhat anxiously, we came down to earth some minutes later and continued apprehensively with the remaining sessions. These included a drill to carry a 'body' down a wheeled escape ladder, the 'body' being a reluctant volunteer from the squad. Then came a demonstration in which we had to tie over twenty different knots for the examining Divisional Officer whilst relating all their various uses in fire-fighting and rescue work. Finally, each of the squad endured a 'question and answer' interview.

That night, the entire squad along with Bill Groves took to the nearby Goldsmith Arms and imbibed liberally to celebrate the completion of the course. Next morning, through some king-sized hangovers, we all learnt our pass marks; I had qualified with a respectable total. The final parade of the last morning at Southwark, in full and spotless fire-uniform, was a fitting end to the arduous eleven-week physical adventure. The squad wallowed in being 'top group', the envy of the other ten squads still in various stages of training.

That afternoon we said our goodbyes, although several of us were destined for the same fire station. A Brigade van arrived to take three of us, our bulging kitbags and gear, to our first operational posting at Croydon and a probationary period of one year: newly qualified firemen to be let loose in public. Little did I know that my real education was about to begin

3

On Parade

'Parade! Parade, 'shun!' The crisp command echoed down the long appliance room of Croydon Fire Station as Station Officer Slade in charge of the White Watch called out the order. I moved smartly to attention at one end of the row of firemen. This was my first morning parade as a newly qualified fire-fighter and it was change of watch time – that time, either 9am or 6pm each day, when the duty shift of firemen was changed. Upon his posting to an operational fire station, a recruit is attached to a 'watch'; another term coming from the fireman's links with the sea.

The manpower of a brigade is divided into three such watches, one watch (Red) being on day duty, the second (White) on night duty and the third (Blue) on leave. After two full days, the Red Watch move on to nights, the White Watch to leave and the Blue Watch back to day duty, and so on. Thus the right balance of qualified manpower, including drivers, turn-table-ladder operators and breathing-apparatus wearers is maintained, twenty-four hours a day, 365 days a year. Fire and tragedy have no respect for Easter and Christmas.

'Call the roll,' the Station Officer turned to his second-in-command, the Sub-Officer, by his side. The two officers stood out in front of the parade, in undress uniform; the other men on parade were rigged in full fire-fighting gear. Five gleaming red fire appliances stood behind the two lines of firemen. The Sub-Officer grasped the roll-call board with both hands, looked momentarily up and down the two ranks and began to call out the alphabetical list of names.

'Fireman Adams.' 'Sir!' came the rapid reply, and on it went. Most of the twenty-strong White Watch had, like myself, arrived for duty some half-hour before parade time at 9am. Several, though, made parade by the skin of their teeth, including one whom I saw arrive pedalling furiously into the drill yard on his bicycle, leap off and dash for the locker room. I discovered that this man only lived half-a-mile distant from the fire station and had over the years cut his journey down to a very fine art. The time before parade was normally used to clean and polish fire uniform dirtied on the previous tour of duty and the gear-cleaning room would hum with banter.

I had arrived on this my first morning just after 8am, and changed out of civilian clothes in the locker room on the first floor. Then, somewhat apprehensively, I made my way down the stairs to the rows of fire uniforms hanging on pegs all down one side of a long ground-floor corridor, to where I had unpacked my own uniform when I had returned to Croydon from training school several days before. As I pulled on my shining fire-boots several other firemen of the oncoming White Watch approached me and smiled. 'You our new lad? What's your first name?' and the ice was broken. 'Roll call and parade is at the back of the appliance room; listen for six bells, six short rings on the call-out bells.'

This was obviously yet another link with the old days of the ex-seamen fire-fighters. 'Stand alongside me, you'll soon get the routine.'

I tensed as the Sub-Officer came to the lower names in the roll-call and called out a rather muffled and self-conscious 'Sir'. He dismissed the off-going night watch, who stood at one end of the parade, called 'Stand at ease' to the White Watch and then read out the crews for each appliance. My name was called out as part of the Pump crew; on this appliance Station Officer Slade went to emergency calls, and I presumed he wanted to keep a personal eye on a fresh recruit.

After all the crews for the shift had been detailed, the Station Officer walked slowly through the two lines of firemen to inspect their uniform and passed comment to several men.

When he finally got to me at the back, he glanced me up and down, obviously noting my training school spit-and-polished uniform as yet unblemished by real action, and said: 'I want to see you later in the morning, lad. The Sub will see you in.' The Sub-Officer read out notices relating to local road closures and low water-mains pressures in force that day, the parade was dismissed and the crews broke away towards their appliances.

Croydon Fire Station at that time had five appliances attached to it. The Pump Escape (or PE) was the primary rescue appliance which carried a 50 foot wheeled escape ladder, hook-ladders, breathing-apparatus (BA) sets, 1,000 foot of hose, two 240 foot hose-reel tubings wound onto drums and fed from a 300 gallon water tank on the appliance, and a host of breaking-in tools and gear and other small equipment. The Pump (or P) was the workhorse of the Brigade. Like the PE, it had a pumping capacity of 1,000 gallons per minute. Its equipment was also similar, except that instead of the wheeled escape it carried a 35 foot extension ladder. The Turntable Ladder (TL) was a four-piece hydraulically operated 100-foot ladder that could rotate about its base and provide either a 'staircase' down to safety for trapped persons, or a 'water tower' – used to project a water jet into a burning building at roof or upper floor level.

The Emergency Tender (ET) was a coach-like appliance that carried additional BA sets, together with many power tools for use at 'special service' incidents, powered by a built-in electrical generator – virtually a travelling workshop. The Foam Tender (FT) was used primarily for the mass production of foam for use at large-scale oil and spirit fires. All these appliances carried minimum crews, the PE five men, the P four, the TL two, the ET five and the FT two. All were normally in charge of an officer, who rode in the front alongside the driver.

After the parade, I took off my fire-uniform and placed it in the rear cab of the P. The uniform consisted of a navy melton-cloth double-breasted tunic, a fibreglass helmet and black waterproof leggings worn over leather fire-boots. From the leather belt hung a leather axe-pouch with axe within and a 12 foot length of light cord wound up bobbin-style and known as a 'belt line'. These personal lines were meant to be kept clean and at first I resorted to Blanco whitener to achieve the right effect. I very soon discovered that when manning a hose-line at drill with much water being sploshed around, I ended up with a tunic-front streaked in white. Worse still, the line itself broke when I had occasion to use it at an incident, and from then on I always kept a duplicate length of cord in my inside tunic pocket, treating the belt line proper as purely decorative and ornamental.

Although my unmarked fire-uniform identified me as a raw recruit, my around-the-station rig – denim overalls – had already had the newness washed out of them and made me feel less of a 'rookie'. All recruits at Southwark had been issued with a considerable amount of kit and uniform, including three tunics and two pairs of fire-boots. I also had a smart undress uniform for routine outside work and visits.

A junior officer of the watch, Leading Fireman Tilling, spent some time showing me over the five appliances and the various equipment carried in their lockers, and taking me on a quick tour of the station. I saw the two stainless-steel poles that connected the first floor to the appliance room, and the watch-room into which came all the emergency calls that the station answered. On the wall in every room and area of the station were call-out bells. The anticipation of my first fire call kept my nerves tingling but my first hour of duty brought no 'shout', as emergency calls were termed.

The Sub-Officer instructed me to report to the 'Guvnor's' office. The entire White Watch was commanded and managed by Station Officer Slade. The Sub-Officer and three Leading Firemen completed the officer complement of the watch. All promotion in the Fire Service since the National Fire Service of the war years had been through the ranks.

The Guv was seated at his desk with papers strewn around the top. Despite a gruff 'Come in!' he had a warm smile for the most recent recruit. He was, however, much to the point as he explained the standard of proficiency I would have to attain in order to have my appointment confirmed in a year's time. 'Remember, no two fires or incidents are the same. Keep your eyes and ears open and learn from your own observations and those of your officers and the rest of the watch. You'll learn a little about human nature, too.' And, looking back over the years, he was absolutely right.

Being detailed to join in the morning drill session, I reported to the Sub-Officer out in the yard, feeling that all eyes were on the newcomer. The drills seem to take place at a gentler pace than at Southwark, and whilst I became involved in the various activities up ladders I forgot that at any moment I could be on my way to my first fire-call.

The fifteen-minute break or 'stand-easy' in the shift at 11am was a time to relax in the mess. This was a large dining-room on the first floor, full of tables and chairs, and served by a sliding hatch to the kitchen. On one wall was a large green-baize-covered notice board, full of Brigade order papers and instructions, notices of off-duty sports activities and dances, and a poster proclaiming a fund-raising charity event. On the opposite wall was the usual call-out bell. I sat down and warmed my hands around a steaming mug of tea and munched a thick but tasty cheese and sliced onion sandwich. Peter Tilling sat beside me and told me these were somewhat traditional to the Fire Service. It was a chance to talk a little more easily to him and some of the other firemen at the same table.

Then it suddenly happened, just when my defences were slack. The call-out bell above us clanged out its alarm and in instant reaction all the men, including, surprisingly, myself, jumped up amid a squeal of pushed chairs and tables and headed for the two poles close by. This was really it! I felt like 6 feet of jelly! As I went through the inward-opening doors that gave access to the pole, I took hold with both hands and feet and slid rapidly down the 20 foot drop into the appliance room below. I tried to remember the training-school drill and got off the mat at the bottom just in time so as not to lose my fingers as another fireman descended right above me. The rest of the watch moved quickly to the waiting fire appliances. All five of the indicator lights, which hung from the ceiling to show the crews which appliance was being called out, had lit up. By this time the drivers were in their seats and engines were started. Headlights became alive and the blue flashing lights on the roofs of the appliances sent reflections bouncing around above the animated scene in magical urgency. Alongside the P, I tried to pull on my boots and leggings, which in the face of mild panic seemed to resist my efforts. I hauled myself up into the back cab of the appliance, right behind the driver, and continued my struggle.

Station Officer Slade, having received the teleprinter slip from the watchroom which showed where we had to go, climbed on board and the P moved off across the fire-station forecourt in pursuit of the PE which had already accelerated away. The other appliances followed in convoy behind. I became aware that the firemen on either side of me in the cab were fully rigged already; they grinned at me as I wrestled with my tunic as the P heeled over into a corner at speed. 'It comes with time,' said one, calm as if this was a bus ride. 'You'll get the hang of it.'

The Guv glanced back into the rear cab and called out above the engine noise: 'Queens Road hostel – automatic fire alarm actuating – the ground floor.' I nodded in silent acknowledgement.

As well as the two-tone horn, the bell situated on the appliance roof was being rung vigorously, giving off strangely flatter tones than when heard from outside. The purpose was not only to clear a way through heavy traffic, but to tell any person trapped by smoke or flame not to jump from windows, experienced help was at hand.

The P seemed to be going very fast, its engine revving hard through the gears and in the back cab we were swung about from side to side. Through the partition in front, I could see over the driver's shoulder and watched the PE forcing its way through the mid-morning traffic ahead. Soon the P swung into the grounds of the hostel in Queens Road. I jumped down from the appliance and saw activity at the entrance to the three-storey building in front of us, although there was no smoke and certainly no fire showing. In the distant background I could hear the fire alarm ringing. Station Officer Slade gave a curt instruction for the main block to be searched and I set off with the three others of the P crew, carrying a 2 gallon water extinguisher. The training-school teaching had said: 'Never enter a building empty-handed.'

Within ten minutes the entire hostel had been checked and no fire discovered; the alarm had been caused by the accidental breakage of the glass of a fire-alarm call-point. The hostel staff calmed the groups of agitated elderly patients assembled outside the main entrance and edged them back into the building and their twilight world. As I came down the stairs with the rest of the P crew, a little old lady in a dressing-gown, grey and tired-looking, confronted me: 'Are we all safe, young man? Can we go back upstairs – is it all right now?' I paused and wiped the sweat off my forehead, for despite it being a chilly March day, I was warm inside my tunic. 'Of course you can, love. It's been a false alarm. Everything's fine. There's nothing to worry about!' The old lady smiled at me, linked arms with a lady friend in the gathering nearby and together they tottered off towards the stairs.

I turned and went through the hostel doors into the drive outside and caught up with the rest of the P crew. Turning briefly to look back up at the hostel building, I saw the two ladies waving down at me from a window. I waved back and then made for the waiting appliance.

Back at the fire station, a pleasant smell of lunch permeated the building. No sooner had the crews peeled off their fire-gear when the bells went down again, this time a call for the P only, to a chimney fire on the council estate.

There was the same scramble to get rigged and get aboard without delaying the turnout. After another hectic dash through the traffic we turned into a street with a smoke haze hanging low from side to side: a chimney stack was vomiting dark-yellow smoke and fiery sparks. The Guv directed the attack on the chimney fire from the grate of the lounge, where we had assembled the 'chimney gear': a number of stout flexible wooden rods that screwed together headed by a length of hose-reel tubing with a special water-spray attachment, pushed up the flue chimney-sweep fashion, until the spray fitting was at chimney-pot level. Water was applied judiciously during the entire operation, either from a stirrup-pump in the room or from a connection to the P hose-reel supply.

At a chimney fire, great care is needed to contain the soot and dust that falls down a flue and the contents of the room were carefully covered with sheets before fire-fighting operations began.

Within half an hour a 'stop' message had been radioed to Brigade Control, informing them that the incident was under control. The chimney fire was out and only a faint and occasional plume of steam identified the still-hot brickwork of the flue. It was easy to understand how, as we had been told at training school, a chimney fire can endanger an entire property by flame or by conducted heat igniting any exposed timbers projecting into a flue.

Seven buckets of smouldering soot were removed from the hearth and after we had cleared and mopped up as best we could, the woman householder thanked us profusely. We washed the worst of the soot off ourselves at one of the water deliveries of the Pump outside before we booked mobile on the radio again and headed off for a belated lunch.

At the station again, after a shower we managed to eat that rather dried-up meal, my first taste of 'hotplate' food. Normally at a station, personnel pay into a collective fund to buy their food, although on day duties a cook's services are provided. On this occasion the cook had served the meal up and that of the Pump crew went onto the hotplate.

During the afternoon of that first day duty, I went on two other calls, both involving vehicles. A fire had started under the bonnet of a saloon car when the driver started up and drove off. Either an electrical fault or a petrol leak had caused it and he was able to get out and call the Brigade. Unfortunately, by the time the PE and P had arrived, only minutes after, the car was a blazing mass. Although the intense fire was soon put out with a powerful water jet and fine spray, the car was a total loss.

Upon our return to the fire station, the several lengths of 75ft 2¾in diameter hose used at the car fire were washed down by the Pump Escape and Pump crews, inspected for damage and then hoisted up the internal shaft of the drill tower to dry in a warm-air current.

While this work was going on, the last call of my first shift came in – to a road traffic accident (RTA) just off London Road, West Croydon. A three-ton lorry had careered across the road, demolished a low brick wall and buried its nose in the front room of a terraced house. When the P screeched to a halt, I saw the spreadeagled lorry with bricks and debris strewn everywhere, and expected the worst. The driver *must* be dead, I thought. The Guvnor had called out for the first-aid box and as I ran with it towards the lorry, I racked my mind for the training-school teachings in first-aid. The driver was slumped over the steering wheel, still conscious but bleeding from deep cuts on his face. The windscreen had shattered upon the impact of the crash and his hair was covered in tiny fragments of glass. No one else appeared to be in or under the lorry, nor was anyone in the house at the time of the crash.

The driver was trapped by the foot pedals which had bent over his feet, and the ET crew drew up close by and soon had their power-cutting tools to work. Once freed, he was quickly lifted out of the bent and twisted cab and into a waiting ambulance. Quite a crowd had gathered to watch the rescue work and were held back behind the police cordon.

The building had to be shored up before the lorry was pulled out by a heavy breakdown vehicle an hour later and the incident was finally left in the hands of the local council surveyor and police.

When the Pump returned to the fire station it was around 5.30pm and the Blue Watch were beginning to arrive for their night duty. It was time to wash yet again and rig in undress uniform in time to be officially relieved at 6pm parade. Then fire uniforms were hung up again amidst the long racks of helmets, tunics and boots; my spotless outfit of nine hours ago was now splashed with dirt and dust. By 6.15pm, in civilian clothing, I could walk over to my car and head home. Passing the glass-fronted doors of the fire station in Old Town I could see the five waiting appliances inside and several of the Blue Watch firemen moving around on their equipment checks.

Whilst I paused at traffic lights down the road, I felt that I could not wait to get back on duty the next day. I was unable to judge if that first nine-hour stint as an operational fireman had been anything like an average shift, but it had lived up to its promise. It had been a day of new routines and a little excitement. I had seen a fire and some blood and cheered up two old ladies.

It added up to a satisfactory first day, by my reckoning, one that I did not really want to end. But as I settled into my new role over the shifts of that first week on duty it was hard to relate the quiet methodical process of station routine, the drills, lectures, cleaning and testing of equipment, to the pandemonium erupting in the event of a call. I went about my duties slightly on edge, in gentle anticipation of the call bells.

The watch as a whole were pleasant enough men, and most went to great lengths to welcome another recruit from training school. Of the officers of the watch, I saw little at first of our Station Officer, who as the operational and managerial head of the watch spent most of his time in his office grappling with day-to-day problems. Drill sessions were usually supervised by the Guv's immediate deputy, the Sub. Two of the watch junior officers, both Leading Firemen, were good company to me. Both were almost exact physical opposites. George Fisher was nearing his retirement, in his mid-fifties, having spent over twenty years as a fireman. Only 5ft 5in tall he was the shortest fireman I have met. He had joined the local Brigade before the war; like all others it was nationalised into the National Fire Service in 1941 and George was thus a veteran

of the blitz fires. Grey-haired, assertive, George was a character
and at drills or over a meal in the mess would pass on a wealth
of Fire Service information to me, frequently illustrated by
exaggerated and jerky movements of his hands. 'Remember
lad,' he would say, 'When you're out working at an incident,
an inspection or a visit, you're frequently in the public eye.
Don't be caught looking like a Rob Wilton fireman, put on a
good show and where possible talk to the public. They're
mostly ignorant of our job, try and do your bit to put the
profession over.' George would then pause to consider his next
words: 'Remember, this job and its future is partly in the
hands of you youngsters. It'll be what you make it, just what
you make it!'

George was the epitome of an older generation of proud
firemen, experienced and full of tales of various exploits, yet,
like the rest of the watch, always ready to see the funny side
of life.

By contrast Leading Fireman Peter Tilling, 6ft tall and in
his early twenties, was typical of the many ambitious, keen
young men who were gaining promotion at that time. He too
was friendly and anxious that I should settle into station
routines and Fire Service life as easily as possible.

Of the firemen of the watch, they ranged from men with
twenty-years-plus service right down to several fellows younger
than myself. As we sat around the mess table at supper-time
on my very first night duty of fifteen hours, I tried to relax a
little and took in the family atmosphere, already aware of a
sense of belonging. The silent fire-bell on the mess wall
dominated the room and I was conscious of the instant shatter-
ing effect it might have at any moment.

Earlier, between 1830 and 1930 hours, I had taken part in
a drill-session in the cold, floodlit drill-yard, where I had been
one of a crew who pitched the 50 foot escape ladder into the
third floor of the drill-tower and then laid out hose-lines that
were hauled aloft to extinguish the imaginary fire within the
tower. I glanced in envy as some of my watch-mates donned
breathing-apparatus sets, which I was not yet qualified to

wear, and saw them ascend the extension ladder to another floor to attack the spreading inferno. At drills and exercises firemen invent the most awful and masochistic fire and other situations, in order to exercise and develop their skills and equipment to the utmost. I ran around and changed some damaged lengths of hose feeding the fire-fighting jets of water working on the upper floors and tried to avoid the soaking I knew was to come. My younger watch colleagues had already forewarned me: somewhere in the water main were a few gallons of water which had my name on them.

Being struck in the back with the full force of a water jet directed from two floors up the tower working at 100 pounds per square inch was a singularly deflating experience. I had ventured across the drill-yard at the base of the tower and had paid the price of youthful folly. The icy water rapidly permeated through my thick fire-tunic, ran down my neck and back and quickly proved the water-tightness of my boots – from the inside! I looked up through the water as it cascaded off the brim of my helmet at the grinning crew on the hose-jet above, thankful that I had only been subjected to this initiation for a few seconds, their jet was now trained away. Everyone, including the Sub in charge of the drill, appeared to be smiling at my dripping form. He then gave the cryptic order for the drill equipment to be 'made up' and put away at the double, and then turned to the aquatic. 'You all right? Get inside and get into a dry set!'

Soon after supper the first call of the shift came in – a fire-call to a department store, which upon our arrival transpired to be a malicious false alarm. For the first time I experienced the sheer and utter frustration of a 'mickey', as malicious calls are unofficially termed. Precious minutes wasted searching a premises for signs of smoke or fire, twenty firemen and several appliances tied up fruitlessly. Somewhere, possibly quite close by, some senseless person watched, the perpetrator of the call. Sadly, I soon discovered that malicious calls to the Brigade were quite frequent.

When the appliances returned to the station I peeled off my

fire-gear and headed for the open-plan upstairs dormitory, laying out my things on a bed adjacent to my personal locker. A fireman's routine allows him to 'stand-down' between 2000 hours and 0645 hours the next morning; during this time he can relax, read, study, watch television, indulge in table-tennis, snooker or darts, and then can sleep after 2300 hours, although he must remain dressed and ready to respond to the call bells; lights come on automatically in the event of a call during the hours of darkness. I had not long completed my bed-making when Andy, one of the younger firemen approached me. 'Taken the tower light up yet, Neil?' he enquired. 'Tower light?' 'Yes. The aircraft warning light on top of the drill tower. It's part of the final night routine of the station. Use the internal staircase and wear a reflective jerkin, so as I can see whereabouts you are if we get a shout.' He proffered me a red hurricane lamp. 'Off you go, quick as you can.'

Now the drill tower was 100 foot high and aircraft were constantly flying over, day and night. Although I suspected yet another wetting, I headed off to my probable doom, expecting the rest of the watch to waylay me before I had half-crossed the darkened drill-yard. However, unmolested I puffed my way up the flights of steps to the top of the tower, placed the lamp out on the flat roof, lit it, and then signalled with my torch the completion of this task to the instigator below. When some minutes later I had descended back into the station, I realised that my entire progress in this buffoonery had been witnessed by almost the whole watch from the windows of the warm recreation room below me. I believe almost every successive Fire Brigade recruit over the years must have fallen for a variation of the tower-light stunt and I had been no exception.

By midnight, most of the watch had turned in. Separate night quarters were provided for the Station Officer on the ground floor. Up on the first floor the firemen's dormitory and locker room had a languid air; men sat up in bed and read, others smoked and chatted, the rest pulled their Brigade-issue grey blankets over their heads, flicked off the bedside lamps and tried to slide off into a settled state of sleep. I personally found it difficult to relax. Like the rest of the watch, I had climbed into bed in overall trousers, navy service jumper and socks. My shoes waited for instant mobilisation alongside my bed. Everyone's fire-gear was either on board or alongside one of the five waiting appliances in the darkened engine-room below. Eventually, after what seemed an age, the very last light in the dormitory went out and I listened to the occasional snuffle or subconscious groan, and the creaks of the metal bedframes. There was the inevitable snorer, but fortunately he was at the distant end of the rows of huddled and horizontal firemen. I tossed and turned fitfully.

At about 0130 hours the lights of the dormitory dramatically flashed on, the call bells were pounding out their tinny din and human forms were rising like wraiths in slow motion from their beds. As my body engaged my mind, I pulled on my shoes, hitched up my overall trousers and joined the accelerating stream of men heading towards the poles. It all seemed harsh yet dreamlike as I progressively woke up with every new step. Down the stainless-steel pole in my fastest-ever descent and out into the large and brightly lit appliance room, I only then realised that the indicator lights were showing ET only. I moved out of the path of the men now running towards the ET and assisted the operation of the appliance-room door mechanism as the officer-in-charge of the ET crew had the address slip handed to him. It was an RTA call on an adjoining fire-station area. Inside forty-five seconds of the rude awakening the ET, its blue beacons penetrating the cold, crisp air, pulled across the station's frosted forecourt and headed off into the night.

I helped to close the heavy doors and then followed the noisy trail of the others back upstairs to the dormitory. One by one the lights went out again and as I slipped my shoes off and slid down between the still-warm ruffled pile of blankets, my heart pounded like a timpano drum. I tried to imagine the horror of the road crash that the ET was attending and wondered if the appliance I was riding would be the next to respond to a night emergency.

No other calls came during my first night duty. I was still awake when the ET crew returned about two hours later and saw the distant lights of the mess go on as the crew brewed tea. They eventually crept into the dormitory on tip-toe and apart from a few coughs and a face momentarily like that of a spectre as a cigarette was lit, that was all the animation I remembered until 0645 hours, announced by six brief rings on the station call-bell system.

The watch made up their bedding, grabbed a quick cup of tea in the mess and spent three-quarters of an hour on routine checking and cleaning of appliance equipment. There was also clean hose to be rolled up and the ET crew checked and serviced some of their power-cutting tools. There was then just time to have a wash and a shave before sitting down to a hearty breakfast. In the mess, against the hubbub of watch conversation and the radio news bulletin, I learned that the ET call had been to a sports car that had careered off a fast stretch of road and hit a lamp standard. The driver was obviously dead and the ET crew had set to and freed a girl passenger, still conscious yet badly injured. It had been a desperate battle with the crumpled front-end of the car and the girl was finally extricated after thirty minutes of frenzied activity by the ET crew and men from the station on whose 'patch' the crash had occurred.

Despite a graphic and somewhat gory description of the only activity of the night hours, the duty had been a severe anticlimax for me. As if to allay my disappointment, George Fisher said: 'Remember young man, you've twenty-five years to do yet. Every time we turn out, especially at night, someone is probably suffering and you'll see plenty of that before you're through!'

4
Of Life and Death

Within a month of being operational I had attended a fair number of emergency calls, although of these only a small proportion had been 'working jobs'. Two however, were classic examples of a special kind of human carelessness.

There was an elderly smoker, who sat up in bed late one night, puffed away at a cigarette and then slowly dozed off. Some ten minutes later he awoke to find his bed burning beneath him. When we arrived, soon after, smoke was pouring from around the frames of the upper windows of the little terrace-house. Although the fire was only a smouldering one within the body of the mattress, I was astounded at the prodigious volume of smoke produced. Breathing-apparatus crews rapidly took a hose-reel up the stairs, having first been assured by the shaken smoker outside that no other persons were involved in the house. Once the mattress and bedding had been located in the thick black murk, the crews had given it a gentle 'drink' with the tubing in order to contain the fire within, and then rolled and bundled the smoking mass out through an open window to other waiting firemen below. As it fell, it burst into flame like a dying meteor. On the ground, the mattress was cut open and the fire extinguished; the windows of the house were opened and the premises ventilated.

The smoke damage upstairs and especially in the man's bedroom was appalling – long traces of smoke-stains and streaks marked the walls and woodwork, the ceilings were completely matt black and every little ornament and memento lay under a coating of solidified fire-fumes. One wondered if

49

the shock of the damage would have put the poor man off smoking for good, but no, there he was surveying the scene with a trembling cigarette between his lips! Even then all those years ago, carelessly discarded cigarettes and ends were one of the principal causes of fires, and the same situation exists today.

Another call during this early stage of my career was to a fire in a café around breakfast-time. A woman helper had apparently left a large frying-pan on a lighted gas stove and then gone to attend to a customer. Several minutes later, the fat in the pan spontaneously ignited and flared up. The woman in panic picked up the fiery mass, intent no doubt on quenching the pan under a cold tap at the sink, but the intense leaping flames and the backdraught of her rapid movement caused her to drop the pan on the floor. Immediately the burning fat spilled out over the already greasy mats of the café and fire leapt across the floor. The woman and the rest of the staff, together with the customers, fled out into the street and some-one called the Fire Brigade.

Half an hour later the fire was out, although the sombre burnt-out and smoking shell of the café was a sad testimony to the woman's folly. Had she left the burning pan in place, turned off the gas and covered the flames with the pan-lid or a dampened towel, there would probably have been at worst only smoke damage and a blackened pan. Now, not only was the café gutted but part of the owner's living accommodation above was damaged, as fire and its attendant heat and smoke products always rise and invade staircases and upper rooms. The poor woman herself had been found, partially hysterical, by two of the watch in the rear yard, the skin of her legs and forearms hanging in shrivelled strips. Moreover, during the fire-fighting operations, a colleague working alongside me was struck on the hand by a falling slate as fire broke through part of the roof, and his wound required twenty stitches.

Other calls during my early weeks were to a couple of minor car crashes, a leakage of acid from a tanker, several lifts full of people 'stuck' between floors in office buildings and high-rise flats, flooded basements and numerous automatic-fire-alarm and other 'good intent' calls. A common example of the latter was a call made after smoke had been seen hanging over an office block; it was discovered to be only the oil-fired boiler 'flashing-up'. At some of these 'good intent' calls inquisitive passers-by would ask 'Where's the fire?' or 'Had your card session disturbed?' I quickly learnt to cope, by jest, witticism or the occasional blunt remark and could, like the others, explain to people just why four appliances and several firemen were hanging around in the street outside a tower office block whilst others searched the labyrinth of rooms and corridors within.

So far I had not seen a fire fatality, although as a recruit one heard lurid tales of charred bodies. My first fatal fire came one cold winter's day. Around lunch-time came a fire call to a seedy, rundown, overcrowded tenement area where every fire call was potentially serious. From my place in the back of the Pump I looked over the driver's shoulder as the PE swung into the street of the call and saw angry fire and smoke coming out of a ground-floor front room of a house halfway down. A little crowd had already gathered and my adrenalin flow increased to a positive flood. With precise judgement the PE driver halted the appliance to give the crew maximum advantage of the road camber to pitch the 50 foot wheeled escape to a third-floor window from which a coloured woman was frantically screaming. Out of the window behind her drifted dark-yellow smoke. The two crews moved like lightning about their tasks, directed by our Station Officer. The escape ladder's wheels crunched down on to the road surface as its crew heaved it off the appliance, turned and extended it skywards to reach the frenetic form now half-hanging out of the smoking window. One of the escape crew called up to the imperilled woman: 'Don't you jump, do you hear? Hang on, we'll get you. Hang on!'

Suddenly, the woman stopped screaming and yelled out: 'There's my kids downstairs; three kids. Oh God!' She resorted to a high-pitched scream again.

Lockers flew open on the appliances, hose-lines were pulled out and two firemen struggled into their breathing-apparatus sets. From down the street came the metallic clang of a fire-hydrant cover being opened as the P's water tank was connected to the mains water supply. The P driver manned his water-pump controls ready to supply the first fire-fighting jet. Adding to the pitch of the drama was the sound of the escape-ladder winding mechanism going full song as the ladder top neared the frantic woman. I had been instructed to lay out a hose-line from the P in order to knock out the worst of the raging fire in the ground-floor room which would allow a rapid search by the BA crew of the rooms at the back of the house and on the upper floors, now all smoke-clogged and hot. As I ran out the hose-line, I was impelled by a sense of urgency I had never before experienced. I snatched a glimpse up at the woman and saw her arms stretched out appealingly like a stark puppet of a Punch and Judy show. The escape crew had almost got to her.

The first jet bore on the intense fire in the ground floor and as it began to disappear, reluctantly at first, the nozzle crew, myself among them, were completely enveloped in the swirling mist of steam and smoke. With the Guvnor's cry of 'There's three kids in there!' ringing in their ears, searching firemen swept past us and fought a path up the stairs through the blistering heat and stinging smoke. We edged our way, foot by foot, through the doorway of the downstairs room and into the torrid atmosphere within, half expecting any moment to feel a tiny soft form. By now the rescued woman, apparently the mother of the missing children, had been safely assisted down the escape ladder at the front and in a state of shock was awaiting removal to hospital. A fireman tried to reassure her as she lay sobbing on the pavement a little way down the street. 'It's all right love. Try and keep still.' The woman sobbed pitifully as the young man took his tunic off and laid it over her prostrate form on the grey pavement. 'We'll find them, we'll get them all for you.'

Another PE, its headlights glaring full-on, turned noisily

Firemen resuscitating a child overcome by smoke in a fire in
Southwark, South London, December 1971 (*Owen Rowland*)

into the crowded street, in response to the Guv's earlier
priority request by radio for immediate assistance. This was
closely followed by an ambulance. Suddenly, amidst the rolling
gloom of smoke and steam of the tenement there was a turmoil
and a muffled cry from deep within.

'We've got one – clear the stairs,' a voice called out, and
seconds later a fireman in BA came down through the smoke
burdened by the weight of a small limp form in his arms. He
carried the young coloured child out into the fresh clean air of
the street and laid it down on the pavement, pulled off his
BA facemask and started mouth-to-mouth resuscitation. The
child, a boy aged about six, was frothing at the mouth but the
fireman did not hesitate in his attempt to breathe life back
into the motionless body, laid before him like a rag doll. The
ambulance crew came running up armed with a mechanical
resuscitator and several blankets. The child's mother, only feet

away, started screaming once again and a voice amongst the gathered crowd on the opposite side of the street cried out in anguished torment.

Within seconds another fireman emerged from the smoke and steam of the doorway of the house with a second child drooped across his arms. This child, like the first, had been found under a bed in an upstairs room, seeking refuge from the dense smoke and intense heat funnelling up from below. The unconscious child, another boy, was about four years old and mucus hung from his small snubbed nose as his smoke-stained rescuer carried him straight into the waiting ambulance, which without delay tore off down the street. Another ambulance had now arrived for the grieving mother.

The crew of the reinforcing PE supplemented the remainder of the crews in their final fire-fighting and search operations as the gutted ground-floor room debris was sifted through and damped down and all the likely hiding places for a frightened child were double-checked. With the fire out, every available window in the house had been opened to improve the still unpleasant atmosphere within. A Police Inspector ventured into the hallway, keen to see for himself the fire damage, and in the full glare of the Brigade searchlights he got no further than the crews working at the foot of the charred staircase. 'I can't stand this – you must all have lungs like old boots!' He stumbled out in retreat, handkerchief over his mouth and partially collapsed in a paroxysm of coughing outside. Then recovered, he took up position alongside his two PCs opposite and inside we smiled at each other for the first time since we left the station almost an hour back, and got on with the clearing-up.

It slowly became clear that the third child was not trapped in the tenement. Several hours later we learned that he, the eldest of the three, had in fact run out of the open front door after accidentally knocking over a lighted paraffin heater in the downstairs front room. He was discovered safe and well, some time after. Despite the valiant resuscitation attempts of two of the watch en route to hospital in the ambulance, both the other children were dead on arrival, asphyxiated in the dark and ugly smoke of the bedroom above the fire.

At the fire scene, the clearing-up and damping-down continued. Small pockets of glowing fire in inaccessible parts of the house structure required careful attention; those hot ceilings and plaster that had not crumbled and fallen over the initial fire-fighting and search crews were pulled down. The salvaged remnants of the personal effects of the family, many blackened and dripping wet, were gathered in a pathetic little heap in the centre of the small front garden. Amongst them was a framed photograph of the three children, showing their glistening and toothy smiles breaking through the grimy cracked glass of the frame. Not two feet away stood the blackened shell of the fatal paraffin heater.

Two hours later the watch were cleaning themselves up at the station, and servicing the BA sets and other equipment used. The two men who had found the children and gone on the unsuccessful mercy dash to hospital had returned, subdued at the deaths, and I sensed an air of defeat hanging over the station. I had seen my first fire fatalities, albeit not charred and grotesque shapes found amid the burning contents of a room. At the change of watch, the talk was of the fatal fire and how we had 'lost' two kids. It was almost as if the children belonged personally to us, although of course they had been part of the large cosmopolitan family of people on our 'patch' that we firemen attempted to protect from the ravages of fire, so often the result of carelessness. I hoped that any suffering those two kids had gone through had been brief and minimal.

During my years as a professional fireman I have obviously taken part in quite a few rescues of men, women and children trapped by smoke, flames or occasionally other predicaments. Sometimes hapless people have climbed out on to ledges or clambered on to flat roofs to await rescue. Sometimes they have been hanging out and screaming from an upstairs window with thick smoke rolling out of the room behind them. Upon the arrival of the Fire Brigade, trapped victims so often look poised to jump from the fiery danger within, and from the firemen below up goes the cry 'Don't jump – hang on – we'll get you!' Yet sadly, on occasions people will jump from an upper window at the very moment that firemen swing their rescue ladders skyward. Many such jumpers kill themselves, and the firemen sometimes ask whether if the traffic en route had been less dense they might have been in time to prevent yet another fire tragedy.

The very first fire rescue that I was personally involved with concerned an Asian-looking youth who had clambered through a first-floor window and then shuffled along a narrow ledge outside his bedsitter in Chelsea. His room alongside him was a raging orange inferno and cascading sparks swirled around him. He stood like a crucifix, face outwards to the street, arms outstretched, hands clinging tenaciously to a hanging ivy draping part of the house frontage.

Whilst other firemen in my crew were detailed by our Station Officer to tackle the fire with a hose jet taken up the internal staircase, I and another fireman quickly slipped an extension ladder from the appliance and crunched it against the front wall with the ladder top alongside the young Asian. The other fireman supported the ladder base and shouted up frantic assurances to the lad whilst I rapidly ascended the 15 feet to the ledge. There I held out one hand and guided the trembling youth on to the ladder and down to safety. This was all accomplished within two minutes of the Brigade's arrival at the scene, but once at the bottom of the ladder the Asian started shouting in his native tongue at other occupants of the burning house who had been able to escape from the fire more conventionally down the inside stairs. As far as I could establish he was unhurt although obviously shocked. The Asian seemed

(*Opposite*)
Medium-size fire (4 pumps) above a betting shop in London EC1, May 1970. Firemen inside in breathing apparatus are completing extinction of the fire, their hose lines supported by crews on ladders outside. Note the extension ladder on the right and 50ft wheeled escape ladder in use on the left (*Owen Rowland*)

unable to comprehend my enquiries as to whether he was all right. No doubt he understood little English and I wondered if he had grasped the shouted entreaties during his rescue.

A particular 'multi-rescue' I well recall was at a Chinese restaurant in Queensway, West London, around 5 o'clock one very cold and icy morning in 1973. There was considerable smoke hanging low over the area as the appliances approached the address and there raging in the ground floor of the restaur- ant dining area was a severe fire. Fingers of flame were already beginning to appear around smoke-yellowed shopfront glazing. From high above, in the choking dark-brown smoke that was mushrooming upwards and enveloping the upper floors, came staccato screams. A wheeled escape ladder was quickly brought into action and as the smoke was momentarily cleared by the wind, there appeared two faces at a half-opened window on the top (fourth) floor, harshly illuminated by the white glare of the appliance searchlights trained on the building frontage.

A fireman's primary task is life-saving, and Leading Fireman George Gamble climbed on to the escape ladder and headed up into the smoke to the rescue. Other firemen struggled into their breathing-apparatus sets, others snaked out hose-lines from the Pump to enable the BA crew to attack the fire at its very seat. The restaurant was securely locked up and forcible entry was necessary but not possible until the rescue 50 feet above was completed. If the plate-glass front door had been smashed open, the subsequent clouds of superheated smoke and gases would have engulfed and endangered the drama being enacted above.

Once George Gamble had reached the half-open window, he was able to perch astride the escape ladder and force open the window sufficiently to allow the two occupants of the smoke- filled room to climb out onto the ladder from where they were led down to safety. The two rescued men appeared to be of Chinese origin and wore long white nightshirts. Appearing down the ladder through the swirling smoke, they looked comical in their attire, the whiteness of their garments accen- tuated by the bright light of the searchlights. As these two finally reached street level, I saw two more Chinese descending the ladder, then two more – all similarly clad. Throughout this time George Gamble was still on the top of the ladder, up in the worst of the smoke. After assisting the *twelfth* Chinaman out of the room, he was able himself to wriggle in through the window into the smoky room and check that it was empty. Thankfully, the bedroom door was closed, but George could hear the intensity of the fire outside on the landing as it spread uncontrollably up the staircase from the ground floor. Through the smoke he could see a fiery orange glow breaking through under the door. The intensity of the heat within the bedroom was overpowering and George wriggled back out through the window to the escape ladder and made his way down before he himself became a casualty.

Crews of firemen wearing BA were penetrating deep into the ground floor now that the rescues were over, and their powerful hose jets slowly knocked down the rippling flames; soon the clouds of dense smoke became less ominous clouds of steam. After half an hour of further strenuous fire-fighting, the job was satisfactorily under control. The only casualties were three firemen: one with the back of his hand gashed open on jagged glass, another with electrical burns to his hands and face caused by a dangling live electrical fitting, and George Gamble who had taken a real 'gutful' of smoke up on the top of the escape ladder and no doubt found it hard to believe the total number of men rescued. Viewed from the street, the pantomime procession of oriental gentlemen down the ladder was so continuous that after Chinaman No 6 had got down safely, one was tempted to believe that the stream of nightshirts was somehow filing back into the building and up to the top window to be rescued all over again!

Twelve rescues at a single fire are thankfully rare. I know George Gamble agrees with that.

A rescue of a far different sort, away from a fire scene, awaited a crew from my fire station when we responded to a 999 call to the bedsitter area of Earls Court in West London early one evening. Earls Court is noted for its large number of

Australian inhabitants. When our appliance screeched to a halt outside the address of the emergency call, a distraught young woman directed us into a tiny bathroom on the first floor. From within came a stream of swearwords and, peering around the bathroom door, I saw a man about twenty years of age with straggly long dark hair crouched over the tap end of the bath. His right arm was jammed down a hole between the edge of the bath and the bathroom wall; he continued to yell out, and the girl squeezed around the door into the restricted space of the bathroom with tears running down her pale cheeks. I noticed she wore an identical tee-shirt to the trapped young man and I resisted the temptation to enquire into the cause of the predicament at this stage, but asked her to go back outside onto the landing, to give us room to work. She shook her head violently so that her long hair flew horizontally about her. 'Look dear,' I said sensing an impasse, 'you've got to give us room. Get up on the loo if you must stay.' Immediately she climbed onto the lavatory seat and stood there towering over the scene below, the tears now falling like rain.

Throughout all this, the trapped young man was shouting out for help in what was, not surprisingly, an Australian accent. With our tools now laid out on the floor, two other firemen levered off the side panel of the bath as I tried to support the shaking and trembling youth. His arm was wedged up to the biceps in the hole behind the taps and, once the side panel was removed, I could see with my torch that his hand and lower arm, visible through the spiders and cobwebs under the bath, was badly grazed but not cut. It was going a shade of blue through lack of circulation.

We then attempted to lever the whole bath an inch or two away from the wall so that we could lift the Aussie out but the bath refused to budge. It was an old, heavy cast-iron one and the waste and water pipes held it in quite securely. 'For Christ's sake, get a move on,' he yelled. 'My bloody arm's bursting!'

The girl, who had been standing on the lavatory seat, was reduced to an uncontrolled sobbing. Her tall form slowly bowed over until I had to leave the trapped Aussie and reach over to catch her from falling. Unable to do anything else with her for that moment, I sat her down on the lavatory seat where she wept bitterly with her head in her hands.

Another fireman and I then took the trapped Aussie's weight under each of his arms and tried to ease him up from his doubled-over position. He screamed out again as his arm refused to come out of the hole. The other firemen both wriggled heads under the bath to try to disconnect the various pipes whilst I tried to reassure the poor fellow again. As I crouched between him and the sobbing girl on the lavatory, he quite suddenly volunteered the cause of his problem. 'I was trying to change a light bulb. I stood on the edge of the bath and slipped.' He too now seemed near to tears. 'I reached out to stop my fall and the wooden edge behind the taps bust. My arm jammed straight down the hole.'

He paused, breathing deeply. Perspiration ran down his forehead in rivulets and as I put my right arm under his armpit to further support the weakening man, his cotton tee-shirt felt damp with sweat. 'Hell! I sang out right away,' he went on, 'Jeese, it seemed a bloody age before any bugger came.'

Within several minutes, the plumbing under the bath had been slackened enough to ease the whole bath out 6 inches. Gingerly, we were then able to lift the man's weight up and his right arm slid free. Staggering over the multitude of tools on the bathroom floor, the young man was passed out through the door to an ambulance crew waiting outside on the landing. Although his arm was only superficially grazed, it looked a horrible pallid shade from the biceps down and the ambulance crew quickly wrapped him in a red blanket and led him away downstairs.

We returned to the tiny bathroom to make good the bath fittings and clear up our tools and there, still sitting on the lavatory seat, was the sobbing girl. She appeared oblivious to the fact that the rescue had been finished. 'Is he your boy-friend, love?' I enquired. 'Yes. We had had a row before this all happened. Can I go to hospital with him?' I told her she could but to hurry before the ambulance left. Some colour flashed into her face as she said: 'I think I want to use the loo. Please!' Her expression was now an appealing one and she smiled at all three of us for the very first time during our encounter.

We retreated to the landing and I shut the bathroom door behind me. One of my colleagues dashed down the stairs to hold the ambulance. As we waited for occupation of the bathroom in order to clear up, I thought of that jagged hole about 4 inches in diameter in the wooden ledge behind the bath taps. It seemed incredible that this alone had trapped the unfortunate fellow in such an unusual and painful way.

Then, as I heard the lavatory inside the bathroom flush, once again I reflected that rescues do indeed come in all sorts of shapes and forms.

5
Firemen at Large

When a frantic member of the public makes a 999 call for the London Fire Brigade, the call will be passed as a matter of priority by a GPO operator at the local telephone exchange to one of three centralised Controls. Between them, these Controls mobilise any of the 114 fire stations in the Brigade. The Controls, remote from any fire station, situated at Wembley, Stratford and Croydon, are the result of considerable technological research, development and enterprise.

Before World War II the telephone exchanges routed all emergency calls direct into the stations of most Brigades. The caller was answered by a fireman manning what is even today known as the 'watchroom'. This contained a telephone switchboard and various controls for actuating the station call bells and all the terminal equipment of street fire alarms, much in use in those days. When a call came in, or a fire alarm went off, the watchroom fireman would 'pull down' (sound) the station bells and write out the address slips, and the red appliances would soon be clanging their raucous exit from the station. The watchroom was thus the station's focal point and was never left unmanned day or night. A fireman detailed for watchroom duty did not ride an appliance to fires – he was 'off the run' and had to keep a wakeful vigil, although he was relieved for meals.

As Brigades have grown larger through amalgamation, and very much busier, and with the vast improvements in communications systems, it has been possible to centralise Fire Brigade Controls in order to cope with the increasing workload and to provide a more efficient and manageable system, as well as better fire-cover for an area. In a large Brigade such as London, central Controls were in fact used many years before the war, but these were generally still part of a station and manned by on-duty firemen (or firewomen during the war years). Over the 145 years of an organised London Brigade, fire calls have arrived at stations by runner, telegraph, telephone and now by teleprinter.

The coming of the teleprinter over the past fifteen years has seen the gradual abolition of fully manned watchrooms at fire stations. A fireman nominated for watchroom duties today rides an appliance when a call comes, although it is his primary task to respond to the watchroom teleprinter terminal from Control, and tear off the slips showing the call address, and the required attendance from the station. He must then press an acknowledgement button to tell Control that the station has received the 'shout' (call), and that it is on its way.

The three present-day London Fire Controls are all similar in operation and are manned around the clock by watches of at least nine operators, both men and women, some of the men being retired operational firemen. The Wembley Control is typical of all the London centres and is housed on the second floor of a modern administrative block over Wembley Fire Station. It has a large air-conditioned central room dominated by a large map of the area it mobilises. This is a sector of London consisting of the West End and the West and North-west suburbs. On the map are magnetic discs representing the available fire appliances at the forty fire stations in the sector.

The stations are subdivided into four divisions: A being the West End, D being West London including London Airport, G being North-west London out as far as Harrow Weald and J being broadly North London stretching up to Barnet and Edmonton. The 999 calls for the Fire Brigade to this entire area all come into Wembley Control, where they are rapidly processed and the nearest available fire station mobilised.

In London, as elsewhere in the country, addresses are

categorised into various risk factors. A is rated a high risk, B a normal risk and C is low. D, usually rural areas, is considered to be very low. According to the risk category, a given number of fire appliances will be despatched by Fire Control. Most of Inner London is rated as A, the outer suburbs being B – an A risk 999 call in London will command 3 or 4 appliances, a B 2 or 3, and so on. Additionally, it is a Home Office requirement that all appliances responding to an A risk alarm must be there within 5 minutes of the call; for a B risk this time limit is increased to 8 minutes, right down to 20 minutes for a D risk.

The other London Fire Controls, at Croydon and Stratford, cover similar-size areas. Croydon watches over the GLC district south of the Thames, whilst Stratford's area covers the City and East London. To give some idea of the operational workload of the LFB and its three Fire Controls, during 1976 over 110,000 emergency calls were passed out to fire stations.

When a 999 call flashes into the GPO exchange, it will actuate a priority buzzer. The exchange operator asks 'What service do you require, Fire, Police or Ambulance?' and then obtains the caller's telephone number as he is connected to Fire Control. This information is essential, as distraught or excited callers may inadvertently cut themselves off before the full address has been taken down. Then the Brigade can at least go to the point where the 999 call originated.

The Fire Control operator who answers the emergency call via the exchange sits at a visual-display unit (VDU) and panel of buttons that remotely control the call-out bells of all the fire stations within the Fire Control area. All the address information is put up on the VDU screen together with the type of incident, fire, car crash, etc., whilst another operator alongside revolves a row of alphabetical card-index drums to locate the one applicable to the 999 call. There is a card for all the streets, roads, avenues, closes, crescents and mews in the Control area; Wembley alone has over 33,000 cards. The card shows which fire-station's ground the incident is on, the required attendance and the order of next nearest stations in case the home station should already be out on another call.

Within seconds, the various fire-stations' bells are ringing and the fire-fighter crews are running towards the waiting appliances as the station teleprinter rapidly reproduces the VDU message. Inside a minute of the original 999 call, firemen are homing noisily towards the scene of the emergency.

Normally, upon arrival the Station Officer in charge of the crews investigates and deals with the incident according to the manpower at his disposal – four appliances bring around twenty firemen. If the fire is a minor one, a radio message is sent to Control stating that it has been dealt with. If, however, the Station Officer needs immediate help because of a rescue situation and severe fire, a radio message to Control is prefixed 'priority' asking for reinforcements, and Control despatches the next nearest crews to the scene, together with other appliances drawn from other areas to provide fire cover in the denuded parts of London.

In Fire Brigade jargon a fire is rated in severity according to the number of pumping appliances summoned to it. A four-pump fire in London is usually a one or two room/staircase/roof job in a small shop, office or dwelling. One jet and breathing-apparatus will be used. A ten-pump fire will probably see three jets and BA in use and involve a whole floor or floors in a larger building. A twenty-pump fire is a major incident, with over a hundred firemen present.

If a 999 call is to a road or rail crash, tanker leakage, or a similar 'special service', Wembley will despatch appliances from the 'home' station together with any specialist appliances from elsewhere which may be required. A foam tender will be sent to a petrol-tanker incident and an ET to a car or train crash. The card-index at Wembley contains all the information relating to specialised attendances that the Control operators need. Major buildings, such as the royal palaces, the Houses of Parliament, the cathedrals, will be sent additional appliances, providing immediate extra personnel for searching and fire-fighting tasks. Fire calls to hospitals, too, include an extra PE to cater for the increased life-risk inherent in such buildings.

Linked to all three LFB Controls are the London Ambulance

Service Control at Waterloo and the Metropolitan Police
Control at Scotland Yard. All Fire Brigade Controls can thus
meet radio requests from firemen for an ambulance or police
and likewise accept emergency calls originating from the police
or ambulance crews. A patrolling PC is often the first to discover smoke drifting out of a building at 3 o'clock in the
morning. In addition, the London Fire Controls have contact
with the various Control-rooms of the county Fire Brigades
that border the GLC area. Emergency calls on the borders are
sometimes dealt with by appliances from both authorities, as
each Brigade can provide for mutual assistance if necessary.
Monitoring the overall activity of the LFB is a central Operations Room at Lambeth Headquarters, and here a comprehensive register of chemical or radiation hazards to firemen is
maintained. The first crews on the scene are told about the
hazard via the teleprinter call slip, and any subsequent request
from the Officer-in-charge for full information on the hazard
involved is handled by Operations Room on their separate
radio channel.

Control staff often have difficulty in extracting from an
emergency call the precise and necessary facts about what
help is needed; for the caller is frequently indistinct and in a
state of panic, particularly if his or her own property is burning
or, even worse, if family or friends are involved. Great patience
is needed to gently yet firmly steady a frantic caller and get
coherent information. All this takes valuable seconds and
sometimes minutes before a station is turned out. If a passing
motorist makes a 999 call he may well be a stranger to the area
and unsure of the street or road he is in. More difficulty arises
when the caller thinks he is in direct contact with his local
fire station and says: 'It's just round the corner from you –
next to the George V pub, you know – just around the corner.
Come quickly!'

Even if a call seems irregular, or is made by a child, as many
are, a Control must immediately send an attendance. If a
really serious fire is under way with a lot of visible smoke and
fire, multiple 999 calls to it will be received, all made by

different people inside several minutes. They are seeing the building from varying angles and do the sensible thing. This information is usually added to the station teleprinter call-slip and crews know that the term '3 calls received' means a 'good-goer' is waiting for them. Sadly, it is also not unknown for a crowd of people to stand watching a burning building, all assuming that the Brigade have been called. Delays of many minutes have been known to occur, lives been lost and property unnecessarily damaged due directly to lack of a 999 call; in such instances the building will be well alight and firemen will have their work cut out to prevent a total loss. Such crowds can be openly critical with such harsh remarks as: 'You've taken your time, haven't you!'

Such are the basic functions of the LFB Controls. The work demands relentless vigilance from its operators, who are strangely remote from the scenes of action, linked only by radio to the distant dramas being acted out. Theirs is an all-important and ever-increasing role as emergencies involving suffering, death and material fire-damage continue to increase unabated year by year.

Would-be Rescuers

We are weary, sad at heart,
Never had a chance from start,
Far too late we got the call,
Gave us wrong address and all.

Broken in was large front door,
Giving vent to fire in store,
By the time we did arrive
No one there could be alive.

Charles Clisby

Once a 999 call for the Fire Brigade has been made, it is of the utmost importance for the firemen to get to the scene as rapidly as possible and there is surely no more stirring sight in a busy city street than the clamorous approach of a fire appliance. In the distance, two-tone horns and the sound of the fire-bell herald its dramatic passage. Pedestrians turn their heads, young children are lifted up to see by their mothers. Motorists anxiously scan their driving mirrors for the first glimpse of the appliance with its head and foglights glaring and its flashing blue beacons. As the Fire Brigade driver steers through the gaps in the traffic, swings down the wrong side of the islands and gently eases over the red traffic-lights, there are few red-blooded males watching who would not relish the chance to be at the wheel of the gleaming, dashing machine.

To be a Brigade driver, a fireman must already hold a driving licence and have completed his probationary year. Only then can he apply for a driving course of three weeks at one of the Brigade driving schools. Here, in the charge of a Sub-Officer instructor, trainee drivers, usually in pairs, learn on driving-school appliances. These are all modern vehicles, are diesel-powered with either six-cylinder or V8 engines developing over 200bhp. Some have five-speed gearboxes and the remainder are automatics. All weigh 8 tons and over and are representative of all types currently in operational use within the Brigade.

The driving-school appliances carry basic equipment to enable the instructor and trainees to cope with any emergency situation met whilst out and about. For instance, a driving-school group several years ago literally came across a house on fire, in East London, smoke pouring from its windows. They crawled into the house and rescued several children who were overcome by the smoke. By the time the local station arrived, the driving-school group had the job well in hand.

Whilst on the course, a fireman relearns the Highway Code and all the principles of safe driving. He drives an appliance in dense city traffic and on steep hills, practises reversing into difficult positions and manoeuvring down narrow winding rural lanes, learns the handling, braking and full performance of the machine on motorways. He learns the various 'Brigade Orders' about driving duties and especially the responsibility of an appliance driver when crossing traffic-lights at red: he must stop or be sure that all other traffic has seen and heard his appliance's approach and given way. Whilst the Road Traffic Act does not give any emergency service vehicle the right to cross traffic-lights at red, it does allow them to exceed the statutory speed limit and to sound audible-warning devices when responding to calls. If, as a result of an accident, a Brigade driver does become involved in a police prosecution, he will probably find that a magistrates' court understands the pressures on drivers on emergency calls and if they find him guilty will exercise leniency. Accidents to fire appliances are, however, rare in relation to the number of calls that they answer and the extreme difficulties they meet in heavy traffic congestion. An appliance driver also acts as pump operator at an incident, and at the driving school he will add further knowledge and skills to those he learned during his basic recruit course.

After many hours at the wheel, on the drill-ground in pumping-sessions and in the lecture room, the would-be driver takes a final practical and oral examination supervised by a driving-school officer. If successful, he is qualified to be a heavy-goods-vehicle Brigade driver.

Upon returning to his station, he first drives back from calls in order to gain the feel of his station machines. Then if his Station Officer is satisfied with his knowledge of the district (topography sessions at stations come up regularly in any fireman's routine), the first shift of duty soon comes when the fireman's name appears on the crew roll-call board as a No 2 – appliance driver.

At change of watch and after the crews are detailed to ride the various appliances, a driver arranges his fire-gear around the driving position, as he will drive to calls in fire tunic, boots and leggings. He then checks his machine from front to back, including fuel, oil and water (both in the radiator and the 300 gallon water tank of the appliance). The lights, two-tone horns, mirror, wipers, lockers and the security of all the ladders and other equipment on the roof of the vehicle is inspected. The driver starts the engine, tests the braking system for pressure and then engages the fire-pump. Whilst he goes to the rear of the appliance to operate the water-pump controls, other firemen in the crew pull off some hose-reel tubing from the rotary drums on either side and test the water jet and spray facility. If the driver is satisfied all is well, he shuts the engine off, but leaves the individual switches controlling beacons, headlights, foglights and radio turned on, then finally switches off a single master switch. When the first 'shout' comes in, all he needs to do is flick down the master switch, turn the starter key and the appliance comes instantly alive.

The first call of the shift sounds throughout the station. The driver kicks his shoes off, climbs into his boots and pulls up his leggings in one movement, and pulls on his fire-tunic as he climbs into the driving seat. As the Guvnor jumps in the nearside front door, he shouts out the address to the driver who nods back in silent acknowledgement. Behind, the crew doors slam shut, the driver selects low gear, and over 8 tons of fire-fighting and rescue gear pulls away. Once out on the shout, the driver's sense of urgency is accentuated by the traffic in front parting to create a path for the appliance as it noisily heads towards its destination. He is however conscious of the Brigade adage: 'No emergency is so urgent as to risk your appliance and its crew.' The two-tones blare and the Guvnor rigorously rings the bell; the driver has the precise address of the call in his mind and the route he is taking, bearing in mind the complex one-way system ahead.

He feeds the large steering-wheel through his hands, pushes the gear-selector into fourth, checks the mirrors left and right, then drops the selector back into third, then to second. Ahead is another set of traffic-lights at red and road speed is right down now, all the traffic is stopped and spreadeagled before the appliance. The driver eases the 8 foot wide machine between a bus on one side and a large container lorry on the other. Two-tone horns reverberate noisily off both vehicles as the bus passengers crane their necks to look into the firemen's cab. The appliance's mirrors clear the sides of the narrow gap by inches; then the driver accelerates away from the clogged scene as the Guvnor gives a quick wave of thanks to drivers who have given way. When the machine is swung left at the next turning, where there is more traffic to negotiate, its path is baulked by a 'ditherer' – a motorist unsure whether to pull over, or keep going on the crown of the road. The appliance driver slows down once again, two-tones kept on and bell ringing clamorously, and he only pulls the machine past the obstructing vehicle when its errant driver at last gives way. In the rear cab, one of the crew growls aloud as speed picks up yet again.

The fire call is to the second street ahead on the right and the crew in the back are now calling out the position of the nearest fire-hydrants to each other from an index-book kept in the cab. As they approach, the driver and Guvnor in the front can see the first sign that this may be a 'working job'. Several people are standing out in the main road ahead and pointing agitatedly up a side turning. As the appliance heels hard over into the side road, the driver has no need to look for the house number; thick black smoke is spiralling from an upstairs window and he pulls up hard in a position just past the house. As the crew pile out and set about their work, the driver turns his attention to pumping operations. He stands over his controls and gauges to provide and safeguard the water pressure needed by his colleagues, now crawling up the stairs on their bellies with a hose-reel tubing.

When after some minutes the small fire is out, the fire-fighting crew emerge from the house and grin at the pump-operator. Each must have implicit faith in each other for at the 'sharp end' a fireman who braves the awful conditions to locate a fire wants to be sure the water supply to the jet will not fail him. Indeed, for a fireman to confront a fire and then lose his armament is a frightful and dangerous experience.

Whilst most fire-fighting is physically uncomfortable, firemen suffer most during initial attempts to penetrate down stairs into the thick rolling black smoke of a basement fire. Whether in a large or a small basement, this demands a very special degree of courage from the first crew to venture down into the hot and unknown depths.

The first crew are all wearing breathing-apparatus (BA) and working as a team, a basic golden rule of BA procedure. The three or four firemen gingerly locate the top of the stairs down into the basement, heaving and working the heavy cumbersome hose-line with them. Then the leader, usually a Leading Fireman or Sub-Officer gives a 'thumbs-up' to his mates and receives a similar signal if the team are ready to face the torture they know awaits them below. Their rapid breathing is accentuated by the noisy valves of the heavy and bulky BA sets on their otherwise silent forms.

The crew leader is instantly swallowed up into the heavy, oppressive hot smoke pouring out of the staircase like an angry black whirlwind. Only the jerky movement of the hose into the smoke tells of his presence already four or five steps down the stairs. The second fireman of the crew takes the weight off the hose and moves into the enveloping upward draught of smoke and heat. The third and fourth firemen follow on down. In the dense smoke, they are working totally blind, able only to feel and grope their way down the staircase, the rails and treads of which are already hot to touch. Crouching as low as they can in order to seek the coolest air still present at the foot of the stairs and half-dragging their hose-line with them, the crew really begin to feel the 'heat-barrier' as they descend the stairs still further. The smoke and heat swirls angrily over them so that, although their faces are protected and sealed within the face-masks of their BA sets, their foreheads are already pouring out sweat that trickles and drips uncomfortably off their noses into the bottom of the masks. Such is the dry, scorching atmosphere in the basement that the crews' exposed necks and ears tucked in under their fire helmets are burning as if laid raw by days of desert sun.

The unseen fire somewhere ahead in their path continues to burn, although it may by now be somewhat stifled through lack of oxygen. At this stage, the crew fear the very worst phenomenon that can befall firemen – a 'flashover': a raging ball of sudden fire that erupts from a smouldering source and sweeps across a room with explosive force, consuming all in its path. The four firemen feel the continual build-up of heat and briefly remember two London firemen who, a few years before, died a most painful death after being caught in the midst of such a horror.

Checking his weight on each step of the staircase lest it has become weakened in the fire, the crew leader reaches the basement floor. He crouches, pauses to allow the other firemen behind him to bunch up to him and, having consolidated their descent into the heat, the crew prepare to drive on through the burning, swirling atmosphere. Their brief communication is by breathless and distorted grunts of reassurance to each other through the speech-diaphragm of their face-masks. Once ready, with the hose-nozzle water-spray curtain turned on to help drive back the heat, the crew shuffle forward to start a search of the basement room which they can feel is piled high with boxes and merchandise. They know that the fire may have crept around behind them unseen and cut off their retreat.

Suddenly, through the rolling murk, the leader sees a dim flicker of orange light. The crew jostle and wheel around to bring the hose-line into a position to enable the nozzle-control to be opened, and the other firemen see the angry flames leaping malevolently over stacked boxes in a far corner. The powerful water jet thrusts its cold shaft into the heart of the glowing mass of fire and the crew are isolated in a cloud of vapour and flying fragments of flame. Superheated steam washes over their crouched forms, as they cling to and support the jet, huddling together in physical contact, seeking reassurance and mental comfort in their nearness to each other. As the jet crackles away, the steam increases and the heat seems to be lessening. A reinforcing BA crew arrives armed with a powerful searchlight. Its beam bores a white hole in the thick fog as the joint crews of firemen move forward towards the fire area, to achieve a final victory.

Ten minutes later, the initial crew is relieved by a fresh quartet of BA firemen sent in from the control-point upstairs, and they make their way upwards out of the basement hell. They emerge into the sheer delight of daylight, report to BA control and then peel off their BA sets, feeling the fresh air cool their reddened necks, ears and foreheads. They revel in the luxury of clean air around them and take in deep lungfuls. They look at each other and grin, consciously aware of a job well done, and of the comradeship and teamwork of the past half-hour. Their faces are outlined where their face-masks fitted and, pausing only to slosh off some of the ingrained smoke-stains with cold refreshing water from a nearby P, the crew replace their fire-helmets with the badges of the LFB now covered with a sticky film of smoke. Having recovered somewhat, they head back to assist in clearing-up operations at the scene of the fire.

The safety of a BA wearer is of paramount importance and, over many years of development and usage, many safety devices have been incorporated into fire-fighter BA sets. Some of these have been the direct result of firemen losing their lives whilst wearing sets at incidents.

One such major fire occurred at the Poultry Market of the London Central Markets in Smithfield, EC1 on Thursday, 23 January 1958. Fire appliances from Clerkenwell Fire Station under the command of Station Officer Fourt-Wells had arrived in response to a 999 call made at 0218 hours. It was an icy cold morning, with a crisp frost. A market employee had reported seeing smoke in the vast labyrinth of basement which was used for keeping poultry and game, usually in timber crates and wickerwork baskets. These were stored in the many refrigerated compartments within the basement area, the walls of which were thermally insulated with both granulated and slab cork, bonded together with bitumous sheeting.

Station Officer Fourt-Wells and his PE crew descended into the basement plant-room and opened the door into an access tunnel that ran under the entire market hall above. As they did so, thick smoke poured out and Fourt-Wells quickly ordered a crew to rig in oxygen BA, a similar set for himself and a hose-reel tubing off the nearest appliance up in the

street. An 'assistance required' radio message was sent to Fire Control as the BA crew donned their sets and they along with Fourt-Wells in his set entered the smoky gloom of the tunnel to attempt to locate the source of the fire. The time was approximately 0230 hours.

By this time, an Assistant Divisional Officer had arrived at the scene and Fourt-Wells reappeared to report that his BA crew were still searching for the outbreak of fire. Market officials had suggested that it might be within a cold store at the very far end of the access tunnel. This cold store was secured by a padlock but a key was quickly found and taken down to Fourt-Wells and his BA crew in the basement tunnel. As the fire had still to be discovered and conditions were clearly getting worse, additional appliances were requested by radio.

Soon after it was learned that alternative access to the 'suspect' cold store could be gained down a vertical shaft from pavement level in a nearby street. However, the only key to this alternative entrance was the one already with the BA crew led by Fourt-Wells still in the smoke-filled tunnel under the market. It was eventually retrieved and given to another BA crew who descended down the shaft of the alternative entrance to the cold store. The time was now about 0318 hours.

Meanwhile, Fourt-Wells's BA crew had located the padlocked door in the tunnel and the key was returned to them after the other entrance had been opened. By now, the contents

(*Opposite above*)
The tragic Smithfield fire, 23 January 1958. General view of the Poultry Hall on the first morning of the fire. At this stage the fire was still deep-seated in the basement. Some hours earlier two firemen died deep down in the smoke. Hoses form a tangled mass in the centre of the photograph (*LFB*)

(*below*)
Smithfield, 24 January 1958. The scene of destruction amid the remains of the Poultry Hall when the fire was finally controlled, 40 hours after discovery (*LFB*)

of the oxygen cylinders of three of his crew's BA sets were running low – each crew member could read his cylinder's contents on a pressure gauge attached to the set by the light of the safety lamp which was also fitted. Fourt-Wells ordered these men, a Sub-Officer and two firemen, out and up into fresh air and then opened the padlocked door with the key. Accompanied by the single remaining fireman of his original crew, Fireman Stocking, Fourt-Wells passed through the door and into the smoke of the cold store inside.

When the Sub-Officer and the two firemen made their way up into the street, concern was expressed by other officers over the oxygen supply of both Fourt-Wells and Stocking who were still searching the cold store far below. An immediate search was mounted for the two men using every available BA wearer; even the Sub-Officer and one of the firemen who had just come up from the smoke took off their expiring sets, donned fresh ones and headed back down into the unknown of the basement area.

After considerable concentrated search in the dense smoke by these BA crews, Station Officer Fourt-Wells was found in a cold store partially buried under parcels of meat. The securing body straps of his BA set were found to be undone and his fire-helmet was missing. The mouthpiece of his set was not in place in his mouth and the head-harness to which it secured was also missing. Soon after, Fireman Stocking was found but, unlike Fourt-Wells, he was properly rigged. Both men's oxygen cylinders were empty. The time was 0440 hours. Both men were rushed to fresh air and artificial respiration was immediately applied and maintained on the short ambulance journey to St Bartholomew's Hospital nearby, but to no avail. The two fire-fighters were dead upon arrival.

It was forty hours before the Brigade finally brought the Smithfield fire under control, during which time over 389 appliances and 1,700 officers and men attended. The fire rapidly developed after the loss of Fourt-Wells and Stocking, and flame became visible in the basement roof-voids and the cold-air ducting complex which threaded the entire basement.

Due to the overwhelmingly intense heat build-up within the thick and swirling smoke, BA crews had to be relieved every ten minutes. Even then experienced firemen were collapsing with heat exhaustion after only several minutes' work with their hoses; the basement was becoming an oven.

Many hours after the initial 999 call, the fire eventually broke out of the basement like a volcano erupting and threatened the entire market complex, but the determination of the fire-fighters was unyielding. As day became night, then merged with another fresh day, the shifts of firemen changed and, slowly, the fire was surrounded and finally subdued in the late afternoon of Friday 24th. Up to this time, twenty-six members of the Brigade had been taken to hospital.

The tragic death of Fourt-Wells and Stocking had a profound effect upon the future design of BA sets nationwide. At the subsequent inquest, the Coroner recommended that all BA sets be equipped with an audible warning when the oxygen contents were running dangerously low. Soon after the tragedy, a device that produced a continuous warning whistle was fitted to all BA sets and today, twenty years after the Smithfield fire, our BA sets incorporate many more safety features that make the wearing and use of a BA set as safe as is humanly possible. Hopefully, a tragedy such as occurred at Smithfield will never happen again.

There are two basic types of BA in use in the LFB, the compressed-air set and the oxygen set. The compressed-air version is simpler to wear and maintain, and has a 'demand valve' assembly which delivers air into the face-mask when the wearer inhales. Exhaled air is expelled directly out to atmosphere. The working time of a compressed-air set is about forty-five minutes. The oxygen set is rather more complicated in construction and has a relatively small cylinder which supplies a constant flow of oxygen into a mouthpiece or face-mask. Upon exhaling, the carbon-dioxide element of a wearer's breath is extracted within the set and the residual oxygen is then recirculated to provide a 'closed-circuit' flow. The oxygen BA set will last for up to one hour.

A grimy and weary BA crew wearing one-hour Proto oxygen sets emerges from a stint in a basement fire in the crypt of St Martin-in-the-Fields, Trafalgar Square, August 1974 (*Owen Rowland*)

After completing a recruit's basic course, a fireman stays on at training school and completes a one-week course which qualifies him to wear compressed-air BA only. After the successful completion of his probation period, he returns to undergo another course in the use of the oxygen set. At both these courses, firemen learn the workings of human respiration, how all the various parts of BA sets function, the 'donning and starting-up' drill, and all the many safety procedures in force. These include a personal name-tally left at BA control before entry into a building, that shows 'time of entry'. This allows BA control to calculate the exact time a BA wearer is due out of an incident. The course also teaches the detailed and important servicing, care and maintenance required to keep a BA set safe and ready to wear.

During the BA course at training school, a trainee first wears a BA set in fresh air. He feels encumbered by the sheer bulk and awkwardness of the whole thing - the total weight of a set is about 40lb – and finds the face-mask claustrophobic. Then with growing confidence he negotiates the specially constructed training, searching and crawling galleries and endures his first sufferings as a BA wearer. Working in crews, groups of trainees work sand-filled hose-lengths around tight and awkward corners, learn to negotiate floors with holes burnt through and other hazards in the pitch-dark, climb through narrow windows and wriggle through sewer-pipe sections, some only 2 feet in diameter. They undergo the physical torture of the heat and humidity room – a thirty-minute session in full fire-gear and BA, moving 5 gallon cans filled with sand from one end of the high-humidity room to the other, via some steps in the centre. This effectively simulates the effort of working in a steamy BA job and soon has the sweat running down legs into fire-boots. The trainees learn the searching methods used by BA crews and the guide-lines used to keep personnel linked together when checking especially complex buildings. They are taught 'entrapped procedure', used when a BA wearer has to conserve his supply of oxygen because he is trapped in a building and unable to make his own way out to safety. Each BA set today has a battery-operated 'distress-signal unit' which, once actuated by a wearer, gives off a high-pitched sound that attracts the attention of the rest of the crew.

Then the trainee crews go through the 'rat-run' and the search areas again, this time in smoke and heat conditions. Their slow progress is monitored by instructors in a central Control-room, who can immediately ventilate the training areas and send in assistance to any trainee in distress.

Once qualified in BA, a fireman will undergo regular training sessions at those stations that have a BA facility. Here, as at training school, artificial fire conditions will be simulated, such training being essential to keep firemen well-educated and confident in the safe and efficient use of their life-support systems.

Today, PVC, polystyrene and expanded-foam products are commonplace in home and industry alike and they produce a growing problem and hazard for fire-fighters. When burning, these plastics produce large quantities of insidious smoke that contain noxious and lethal elements, far more deadly than the smoke produced by other types of fire. Because of this smoke hazard, BA sets are now worn at virtually every fire. The days of a 'good' fireman – one who could crawl into a smoky room and work without any sign of apparent difficulty – are over. So too are the officers who ordered their men into smoke without proper regard for the delicate respiratory system of the human body. In those days we coughed, spluttered and took it all in our stride and only got the BA sets off the appliance when all else had failed. Following medical advice, we now put BA sets on as a matter of course and, thankfully, the 'smoke-eating' fireman is gone forever.

BA is also increasingly worn at spillages of toxic and poisonous chemicals, especially when involved in conveyance by road tankers. But this is another story.

6

Some Major Jobs and Moorgate

After eighteen months of operational service as a fireman at Croydon I transferred to the A division of the LFB, which is roughly the West End and surrounding areas. Although Croydon was a comparatively busy station, I sought the wider experience a Central London posting would bring, and over the years I have not been disappointed.

Although the division consists only of nine stations it was, and still is, one of the busiest of the eleven divisions which cover the 610 square miles of the GLC area. Within its boundaries are many major buildings: vast department stores, hotels, theatres, museums, cathedrals and government offices, together with main-line railway termini and a network of underground lines. One fire station, Westminster, is affectionately known as the 'Queen's Fire Brigade', for on their patch is the monarch's London residence, Buckingham Palace. At the north-west of the division many of the immigrant population have made their homes, some in overcrowded conditions. This area in particular is an extremely busy one for us, especially during the cold 'paraffin heater' season.

Because of the complexity and sheer size of some of the buildings involved in the many fire calls, even a minor outbreak often threatens to become a major fire. Fires in hotels full of foreign tourists unfamiliar with escape routes are a constant hazard, and many of the serious fires in the West End over the past few years have involved hotels, sometimes with high loss of life. The many student bedsitter areas too, see their fair share of tragedy, in both fires and suicides. On many occasions

83

the retrieval of the body of a disillusioned youngster has been the unpleasant task of firemen.

The variety of a fireman's work in Inner London is so great that the turn-out of appliances from a station, always a high-pitch of excitement, is a heightened experience because of the sheer diversity and contrast of life which lies outside the fire-station doors. This was well-illustrated by a very busy spell of two weeks during the late sixties when I was attached to Manchester Square Fire Station, just off Oxford Street. One of the varied incidents we attended was a fire that destroyed the electrical intake of the trade-legation offices of a large embassy. As our fire-boots sank into the deep pile carpets, courteous oriental gentlemen bowed and smiled profusely at each of us as we moved throughout the building, ventilating and checking the service ducts on all floors for fire spread. We all felt like ambassadors, which of course from the LFB point of view we were. A charming letter of thanks from the ambassador himself arrived at Brigade headquarters some days later, together with a handsome cheque for one of our charities.

About this time came another reward of a different nature following a large fire in Berkeley Square. So impressed were the owners by our successful efforts to save a historic Adam-style house, once occupied by Clive of India, that they invited fifty firemen to a special dinner in the actual house some weeks later. Suitably dressed and anticipating a splendid alcoholic evening, we sat down beneath the magnificent gold ceiling of the dining-room to discover, to our dismay, that there was only apple juice to drink. Our hosts who provided the superb meal turned out to be a modern-day temperance society. Nevertheless, none of us would have missed it for the world.

On Cup Final night several evenings later, a 'thirty pump fire' occurred in a clothing manufacturer's offices in the trendy psychedelic back-streets off Carnaby Street. At one stage the blaze threatened the entire Oxford Circus area, such was the rapidity with which the fire leapt from one building to another. During fire-fighting operations on a flat roof, totally enveloped in thick swirling smoke, Station Officer Mick Keevash of

Westminster Fire Station fell through a skylight onto a floor below where the fire had not long been put out. He lay semi-conscious and groaning amid the still-smouldering debris until hastily rescued by several firemen of his own crew who lowered themselves on lines through the shattered glass of the skylight. Mick, who had smashed a kneecap, was quickly hoisted out and removed to hospital, where he was detained for some months and underwent several operations. Then with great determination, first on crutches, then with the help of sticks, he walked again. Eventually, after many months, he returned to the full rigorous duty of the professional fireman.

On the lighter side, was a call to 'two persons shut in a lift' between floors at a famous West End gentlemen's club, late one evening. The crews of the two appliances, PE and P, sent to such lift calls, went through the usual routine of gaining access to the lift-motor room on the roof, shutting off the electrical power and then hand-winding the lift car to a floor level and manually opening the lift-car doors. This work sometimes took a little time, and on this occasion the two occupants inside the lift sounded cheerfully inebriated and insisted on serenading us, less than melodically, as we worked to free them. Whilst the work went on, a liveried and brass-buttoned club steward watched over us anxiously.

After ten minutes' effort, the lift car was wound down to first-floor level, its doors opened and the two dinner-jacketed occupants emerged, swaying and leaning on each other, 'By jove, what a thing to happen! Good show men, good show! Officer, what will you and your men have to drink?' 'Well, sir, officially we can't when we're on duty, but. . . .' 'Nonsense man, nonsense, I insist you partake of a little something for us to express our gratitude.' His companion tried to focus his eyes on his rescuers and nodded deliberately in agreement. Before the Guvnor could protest further, the old man waved the frowning steward away to fetch a tray of glasses and ushered all ten of us into the leather-upholstered lounge. As the other aged occupants of the room dozed on, oblivious to the uniformed visitors, we raised our glasses to toast 'the Brigade'. I never did discover who the two noble old gentlemen were, but have never forgotten that night and even today I smile as I pass the doors of this club, where ten total outsiders enjoyed its exclusive hospitality and comforts for a few minutes.

A fire call to a tenement area the next morning took us back to the seamier side of life; a stewpan on a gas-stove had boiled dry and produced a strong smell of burning outside the house. We arrived, prised open the door and quickly located the kitchen where the gas was turned off and the smouldering stewpan removed to the open air. Nobody appeared to be in and our cries around the house went unanswered. During efforts to clear the pungent smell, I went upstairs with another fireman, our 'junior-buck' recruit, to open windows of the top rooms. The stair treads were bare of covering and the noisy clumping of our fire-boots sent two mice scurrying across the landing and into a hole in the skirting-board. In the corner turn of the landing was a cracked sink with a solitary dripping tap. A dark wet stain, edged with mildew, showed where the waste pipe was leaking. To our surprise, when we pushed open a bedroom door off the landing, we discovered two gorgeous young children, both fast asleep in the same cot, and quite oblivious to the commotion down below. The whereabouts of their mother was a mystery and the incident was left in the hands of a local PC. It did not shock any of the watch, except the 'junior buck', that a family should live in such sordid conditions. The rest of us had seen it all many times before.

Another major incident in this busy period was a fire one evening at the world-famous Press Association and Reuter's newsagencies' building in Fleet Street. The fire had started on the seventh floor and already had a good hold when the first crews arrived; fire-fighting was further complicated when it was discovered that there was no 'dry-rising main' – a large water-pipe running through a building, having Fire Brigade outlets on all floors, and charged with water by the Brigade upon their arrival. Additionally, none of the lifts were working, so all the hose-lines had to be hauled up or carried up to the seventh floor via twenty-two flights of stairs. As the fire developed, the large complex was progressively evacuated and the busy floors of telex and teleprinters bringing in news and events from all over the world were reluctantly shut down by the agency staff. This was pre-deadline time, probably the most hectic time of day for Fleet Street. Eventually, the senior Fire Brigade officer demanded full evacuation of the building and this was finally achieved, but not until some members of the agency staff had despatched a cryptic message: 'This is Press Association/Reuters, London, and we are now closing down. The building is on fire. Ends.'

The fire-fighting plan was for BA crews to man hose-line jets at either end of the seventh floor, now heavily smoke-logged, and drive the fire out through the rear windows of the building. This plan however had its hazards, as the intense radiated heat driven out at the rear of the seventh floor might endanger a Wren church in a courtyard close by, and the building's new £20,000 staff canteen on the floor above. Additional crews with hose-lines were placed to cover these dangers, including one group of firemen who had to struggle up the narrow spiral stairs within the church's steeple in order to protect the ancient building from the belching fire from the office block only forty feet away.

After several hours the fire, contained on the seventh floor, was under control, and such was the skill and fortitude displayed by the fire-fighters that the news agencies were back in business only hours after the outbreak.

The subsequent media coverage of this particular job was typical of the reporting of fires and incidents in Central London. Many minor fires or even 'good intent' calls made the front pages of the evening newspapers solely because the addresses of the emergency calls had been the Houses of Parliament, the Covent Garden Opera House or perhaps St James's Palace. Nobody seemed very interested in fires in the slums of North Kensington.

Indeed, when a fire was reported in the newspapers, quite often all the credit was given to people other than firemen. There would be many lines about a brave passer-by who attempted a rescue in the smoking building, but no mention of all the doors he had left open in the process, allowing in vast quantities of oxygen to feed the fire. The report would detail the efforts of the police in controlling the traffic and crowds of onlookers; there would be nothing about the firemen who grappled with the fire at very close quarters. Many reports of major fires I have personally attended have been so distorted and inaccurate in their detail that I have wondered if the reporter had been at the same job as myself.

Some years ago, Mr Hugh Delargy MP was staying at a hotel in Grays, Essex, when a fire broke out. He subsequently wrote in a Sunday newspaper:

What made me marvel was the speed, calm, precision and silence of the firemen. Each went about his allotted job and the man at whom I marvelled most had the job of walking first into the fire. Reconnaissance, we used to call it in the Army; the stickiest job of all. Nobody has ever suggested that these men be given the George Cross. They get paid for the job. Paid so badly that last year hundreds of them queued to see their MPs to ask their help in getting a few extra shillings a week. Half-a-dozen newspapers reported this fire, and they all mentioned me. Reports of my behaviour in the crisis were more colourful than accurate. But I'm not complaining. The inaccuracies were all in my favour. The firemen, of course, weren't mentioned at all!

But sometimes, as the following account of a major disaster shows, the Fire Brigade does get its due share of recognition in a crisis, although the situation may not be in response to a 999 fire call. Cries for help to the Fire Brigade unconnected with fire increase every year, both in number and variety. Firemen learn to deal with these 'special service calls' as they are termed and become skilled in cutting, squeezing and bending metal in car crashes in which people are trapped, pumping-out flooded basements following rainstorms and making safe leakages of explosive gases and toxic liquids. Thankfully, major accidents involving train or aircraft crashes are rare, but much pre-planning and training by all the emergency services ensures that there is swift and efficient response to the natural and man-made disasters which tragically occur from time to time. At major accidents, the Fire Brigade with its equipment and expertise has the task of casualty rescue and recovery.

During my service, two special 'special services' stand out to illustrate the work of the Brigade when involved in a purely rescue situation. The first of these was the Moorgate underground train crash of 28 February 1975.

At the peak of the morning rush hour, a six-carriage tube-train crowded with incoming London commuters, failed to slow down for its last stop at the Moorgate terminus, ploughed through the sand-drag and buffer stops and slammed into the wall inside the dead-end of the tunnel. The front three carriages 'concertina'd' and in a few horrifying seconds many men and women were crushed to death. Many others however, in the packed confines of the front carriages, clung perilously to life despite serious injuries and being jammed into torturous positions, often beneath or alongside inert yet warm bodies. Upon the tremendous impact of the crash, all the lighting in the train and on the platform went out and the whole area was clouded in a thick black dust. Fortunately, no fire broke out.

When the first Brigade appliances arrived soon after the crash, the enormous scale of the tragedy and the task ahead became clear, and the officer in charge of the first crews initiated 'major accident procedure'. In accordance with the prearranged plan, fire appliances, ambulances and police cars were summoned from all over Central London and nearby hospitals put on full alert.

Fortunately, the rear three carriages of the train were quickly cleared of blackened and dazed casualties and a mass assault was mounted to free the many people trapped in the front part of the train. The crushed and tangled red metalwork of the carriages seemed to fill the 70 foot long dead-end tunnel and intially only one fireman at a time could wriggle into the wreck through holes cut in carriage end-panels and roofs, or by worming his way up the narrow sides of the tunnel and into

the train through the shattered windows. As the men crawled into the carriages, they saw in the light of their powerful torches that a number of people were already beyond help, although many others were trapped, injured but conscious. Afterwards, many of the survivors said that once they saw the firemen coming through the wreckage towards them they knew they would get out alive. Sadly, not all the injured did.

All the firemen's power-cutting equipment, crowbars, hacksaws and many other tools had to be passed into the train by the same difficult path. As the morning wore on, the live casualties were released one by one, and manhandled back down through the train and out to the platform where the Ambulance Service took them over for the short journey to hospital. All the firemen were going into the wreckage on a short 'work and relief' system, and young and old crews alike stripped to the waist and worked like Trojans in the ever-deteriorating conditions. They worked under and amongst tons of hanging and mangled metal and slowly penetrated further and further into the mass, but progress seemed excruciatingly slow.

A surgical team from a nearby hospital had earlier set up its equipment on the platform, and doctors frequently crawled into the wreckage to give drugs to a victim while firemen worked on undaunted. By mid-morning, twenty-five trapped passengers had been extricated, although about forty were still pinned in the crumpled front two carriages. Flood-lighting had now been provided in the train and on the platform, and steady progress in the work of extrication was made. Fresh relief crews took over from the grimy night-shift of firemen still at the scene, as more and more men and appliances arrived at Moorgate. By noon, seventy casualties had been removed, but heat continued to build up to add to the discomfort of those

(*Opposite*)
Moorgate, 28 February 1975. Firemen inch their way past the impacted carriages of the underground train in the dead-end tunnel; the working conditions facing the rescue crews were appalling (*LFB*)

91

Moorgate again, showing crews working on the roof of the second carriage of the underground train. The rear of the leading carriage of the train can be seen crumpled up and jammed against the roof of the tunnel (*LFB*)

still trapped and their toiling rescuers. Working in temperatures of over 100°F (38°C), the firemen sweated away cutting, bending and lifting the twisted metal and timber of the carriages. Occasionally with a quiet and reassuring word, they comforted the poor suffering person who was trapped.

After many hours of grimy and stomach-turning work, around mid-afternoon it was clear that only two of those still trapped in the train were alive. One of these, a young policewoman, was hopelessly caught by her foot and, after a valiant struggle to free her, the doctors decided that drastic steps must be taken. A crew of firemen supported the young woman whilst a doctor amputated her foot at the ankle. She was then hustled back through the carriages and an hour later the last live casualty, a young man, was finally released.

Then began the sad task of retrieving all the many bodies still trapped amid the wreckage. Over three days and nights, teams of firemen worked to recover them, while the air in the tunnel became progressively worse. The firemen had to wear filtered masks and gloves as they struggled to free the crushed forms. Later the atmosphere in the tunnel of death became so putrid that the firemen had to don breathing apparatus and any direct contact with a body required a decontamination shower and a set of fresh clothes. Even the tiniest scratch meant an anti-tetanus injection, for the medical advisers present were increasingly worried about the health hazard to the rescuers. By the fourth morning after the crash, all firemen entering the train had first to change their own uniforms for dungarees and wellington boots that were completely cleansed after a crew had been relieved.

As each piece of wreckage was cleared of bodies, it was winched out of the tunnel by railway engineers, and the last body, that of the driver, was recovered from the train on the evening of 5 March. Over 1,000 London firemen were in attendance over the five days and four nights following the Moorgate crash and the final toll stood at 42 dead and 76 persons injured.

At the time of this major accident, I was Station Officer in charge of a watch at Paddington Fire Station and I well recall the return of my emergency tender crew from Moorgate, after its second visit on the first day of the crash. I went down into the appliance bay to greet the seven-man crew, many of whom had only recently qualified to ride the rescue tender. There I met seven grimy, silent and sorrowful firemen; even the Leading-Fireman in charge of the tender, a hardened man of over twenty years' fire and rescue experience was obviously distressed at what he had seen in the tangled tube-train. I later discovered, after they had all taken a shower and picked unenthusiastically at a supper, that they had been the men who had held the last female survivor, the young policewoman, whilst her foot was amputated so that she could be manhandled back through the wreckage and whisked away to the clean air of St Bartholomew's hospital.

Like most London fire stations that week, all watches at Paddington did stints at Moorgate and, on that first evening after the disaster, there was an unusually quiet air throughout my watch. Those who had already been and worked amongst the horror tried to forget and those yet to go tried not to anticipate the conditions that awaited them.

In the days after Moorgate, the many firemen, doctors, nurses, ambulancemen and police, together with other groups who had contributed to the massive effort, received full praise in the media for their work. As firemen, we all felt that just for once our profession in particular received its due recognition, although sadly acknowledging that it had taken a major tragedy to make the point. Amongst the tributes to the Brigade for their part in the Moorgate disaster was one from the Home Secretary, Roy Jenkins.

The City of London Police Commissioner, James Page, commented, 'It was the firemen who had to work all the time in the wrecked train and their courage and cheerfulness came through very strongly to the police who were privileged to see them in action.'

The Chief Officer of the LFB at that time was Joe Milner. He described his Moorgate crews of firemen in an *Evening News* article during that dreadful week as simply 'my thousand selfless heroes'. In that very brief tribute to his own men, I think he said it all.

By way of contrast, the second unusual and memorable 'special service' call received none of the mass publicity afforded the Moorgate horror, for it only involved one Central London fire station and one five-and-a-half-year-old Pakistani boy, Salim.

Like all boys of his age, Salim was an adventurer. His mother ran a shop and while he played near an electric meat-mincer in use he put his fingers into the feeder-funnel. In a split second, Salim's hand was drawn up into the machine through the cutters, until the tops of his little fingers appeared at the outlet; his hand was jammed tight. Very soon three fire

94

appliances, an ambulance and a police car arrived at the shop. Salim was conscious and in great pain but showed no sign of tears to his rescuers. The firemen quickly took stock of the boy's predicament and decided to rush Salim *and* the mincing machine to hospital.

Upon their arrival at the casualty department, Salim was gently laid down on a trolley and the machine laid alongside him, supported by firemen. A doctor examined the poor little boy, who still refused to show his feelings and it was quickly decided that because of the sheer bulk of the mincer, the use of an operating theatre was impossible. The examination room of the casualty department was then rapidly prepared for the extrication attempt. Salim's pain was eased by drugs and still he remained tear-free, although as the trays of surgical instruments were assembled around him he said appealingly to the two firemen supporting the mincer, 'Take it off my arm mister, it hurts.'

Once the doctors were ready, Salim was anaesthetised and the job of sawing through the metal casting of the machine's funnel began. Relays of firemen worked away with a hacksaw and using only very gentle pressure with short, precise strokes, the heavy casting was progressively parted, although extreme care was needed not to cut into Salim's hand and arm. Stroke by stroke, turn by turn, the firemen worked on under the hot bright lights, and after an hour and a quarter, the funnel casting was finally parted. Then by careful turning of the gear wheels inside the machine, Salim's hand was almost free.

Now the doctors were able to examine the entire hand and wrist and quickly indicated that it could not be saved – it was crushed beyond surgical help and would have to come off. The firemen cleared up their tools and left the doctors and nurses to their task, sad that their effort to free the little boy had failed, especially after all his bravery.

The story had two happier sequels. During the next night the same crew of firemen, now on night duty, came to the hospital to deal with a small fire in some piles of rubbish. After it had been extinguished, the Station Officer enquired in the

95

casualty department after Salim. Although it was well past midnight, he was taken upstairs to the ward where Salim lay. The boy was awake. To a whispered 'Hello, Salim, how are you?' came the lad's reply 'I'm all right, thank you, where are all the other firemen?' 'Downstairs and I'll tell them how well you are getting on.' In the dim light, the fire officer saw that Salim's left hand was swathed in a large white dressing and then the sister alongside him ushered him towards the door of the children's ward. He waved farewell to Salim: 'See you soon.' Salim waved his right arm and smiled enchantingly.

The second part of Salim's story took place when he was finally discharged from hospital some months later, and the watch of firemen involved in his release prepared a very special surprise for the coloured boy. Salim was collected from his home in a Fire Brigade staff car and taken to the fire station, where he looked over all the appliances, sat behind the steering wheels, tried on a fire-helmet and watched firemen as they slid down the poles. Then he was taken up to the firemen's mess where he enjoyed a slap-up meal and was afterwards presented with a model fire appliance as a token of the watch's recognition of a very brave youngster.

For once, Salim was a trifle overwhelmed and so too, I think, were some of the firemen!

7

Of Creatures Great and Small

Firemen occasionally come to the aid of various non-human creatures who have become trapped or stuck. I know of many firemen who have rescued cats from rooftops and high ledges, horses and cows from muddy ditches and even a crew who pursued a golden eagle escaped from London Zoo from tree to tree in nearby Regent's Park. There was also a case of a lowly London pigeon which became ensnared in the wires of the tree-top lights of Leicester Square. Using an escape ladder, firemen from Soho Fire Station freed the poor bird, none the worse for its experience.

Normally the Brigade only rescues animals if the RSPCA are unable to retrieve a suffering creature by their own resources. Any 999 call by a member of the public to an animal or bird in trouble is first referred to the nearest RSPCA officers. But if ladders are required, the Brigade usually becomes involved. Sometimes a straightforward emergency call develops into an 'animal case.' I was personally involved in one of these, several years ago, in the Paddington district.

It began as a 'shout' late one evening to flooding in a luxury block of flats. The call had come to us via the local police station where there was a PC who had the happy knack of turning us out to all sorts of unusual incidents; there had recently been a burglar stuck on a roof, a crashed stolen car, and a suicide out of a sixteenth-floor window. Occasionally he found us a fire or two to deal with.

We arrived at this block of flats and there was our PC friend; apparently he had found us a routine job at last. He had been first called to the block when a flat occupier on the third floor noticed water dripping through his ceiling. The PC was unable to raise the occupier of the fourth-floor flat above, but was able to see through its letter-box that water was seeping from under a closed door within. He had then called for Brigade assistance and supposing the very worst, that the occupier might have collapsed whilst taking a bath, duly asked my crew to force an entry.

Our escape ladder was quickly pitched to an outside window of the flat, inside which shone a light. My Leading Fireman ascended the ladder, peered in and then came back down. He reported he could just see over the drawn curtains and that the bath taps were running, although his view was restricted by condensation.

I debated whether to attempt an entry through the closed window off the ladder, or to spring open the flat's front door; deciding on the latter, I took our breaking-in tools up to the fourth floor, accompanied by the PC. As the front door to the flat was being forced open, somewhat noisily, the elderly lady tenant of an adjacent flat appeared and in a very alarmed voice asked what was going on. With diplomatic aplomb, I assured the grey-haired old lady that there was nothing to worry about, although it was hardly surprising that she thought some catastrophe had occurred. A woman PC had turned up and attempted to calm the old lady, who quite suddenly turned towards us all and said, 'I shouldn't go in there if I were you – there's a snake in there.'

The door to the flat had just been forced open and, gripping the handle tightly to keep it pulled shut, I heard this information with senses inwardly screaming. I turned to our PC behind me and he too was ashen white; the WPC was nowhere to be seen at all.

Then, with the door of the flat still firmly closed, I questioned the old lady neighbour; she was adamant that the girl occupier of this flat kept a snake. There followed a traumatic experience as I gingerly entered the flat, the deep carpet already soggy with water under my feet. I turned the hall light on; no snake so far, nor any sign of the girl occupier. Down the hall was the closed bathroom door with water still seeping out underneath; the light inside was still on and a towel was lying along the bottom of the door. Very carefully, I edged it open and in ten seconds I aged ten years. There, coiled around the swamped bathroom floor, was the biggest snake I had ever seen – 10 feet long and a foot in circumference at least. I slammed the door shut and turned around to my crew behind in the hall. From the looks on their faces I did not have to explain the problem; they must have glimpsed some of the reptile through the open door. I heard the muttered rumbling of the PC as he rapidly retreated into the corridor outside the flat.

At this stage, I had still not looked into the bathroom long enough to check if the lady snake-owner was inside and, bolstered by the fact that I was under the critical gaze of my men, I gently opened the door once again to have a better look. 'Bloody hell! There's three of them in here!'

And there were. One, the first I had seen, was even longer than I had first estimated and the other two were about 6 feet in length. All looked exceedingly unfriendly over the intrusion. There was certainly no girl in the bathroom but there was a hot tap running, two sun-lamps glaring away and some article of laundry, no doubt dislodged by the snakes' movement, blocking the bath plug-hole and causing the overflow. Thankfully, I shut the door once more.

There followed a stealthy search of the remainder of the flat and all then started to make sense. We found several photographs of a near-naked blonde with snakes coiled around her form. The girl occupier was probably a club stripper who used the reptiles as part of her act and normally left them in the humid atmosphere of the bathroom.

Our appliance radio was now alive with messages as I asked Control for the urgent attendance of vet, zoo keeper, RSPCA, snake charmers, anyone I or they could think of who might identify and occupy the snakes so that the hot tap could be turned off and the bath unblocked. Water was still running through into more flats on the third floor below! The PC returned to the scene looking even more shaken than when he left us. He told me that he had summoned his Inspector and that the 'nick' were also trying to trace the female charmer who owned the snakes.

In their search of the rest of the flat, two of my crew had discovered a large wickerwork basket in the lounge. It appeared to contain something alive for it was jerking and creaking. Using a steel hydrant-bar, the lid of the basket was lifted an inch or two and there was a baby rabbit inside and we breathed again – that is all except the PC who had once more disappeared. What part of the lady's act the rabbit consisted of, I knew not; the thought that the helpless creature might be the next meal for the snakes appalled me.

Soon after, the police Inspector arrived. After some deliberation, he said that if I held the bathroom door open for him, he would go in amongst the reptiles and turn off the offending tap. Despite my suggestion that it would be safer to wait for advice or knowledgeable handlers, he went ahead and stepped in over the snakes whilst I kept open his means of escape. Three forked tongues flashed angrily at the Inspector as he reached across and turned off the tap and then beat a hasty retreat out into the hall, whereupon the door was shut on the snakes who by this time were becoming cross.

The flooding below was then dealt with and the three snakes left secured in their tropically heated bathroom. Our PC reappeared once again and we left him and his very brave Inspector to sort out the aftermath of the skirmish and to calm the somewhat nervous occupiers of the rest of the flats.

I subsequently discovered that the three snakes were all pythons, which normally crush their prey. Someone on the watch said he had read that a python could swallow a whole pig. Having seen the biggest of the trio at close quarters, I believed him. I mused too on the thought of what would have befallen my Leading Fireman if I had sent him into the bathroom through the outside window from the escape ladder.

Another more recent unusual incident involving an animal followed the Brigade's response to a fire call in a street just off the Edgware Road and not a mile from Marble Arch. The first appliance had arrived and, as no fire was readily apparent, the crews were deployed to search the immediate area. The Station Officer was standing outside the house to which the call had been made, when suddenly a young man came running up, pushed open the front door and shot inside. Before the Guv could converse with him, the door was slammed shut and bolts were drawn inside. A woman, hair piled up in multi-coloured curlers, appeared from the adjacent house and, in a harsh voice, asked what was going on. 'There's been a fire call,' the officer said, 'To your next-door neighbours' place,' and pointing to the closed and barred door, 'Just what's up with him? Is he frightened of firemen or something?' The woman paused, drew deeply on the cigarette drooping from her lips, and glanced up and down the street. 'Well, you see officer, I'm not one for making trouble but he's got a big pussy in there.'

The conversation was cut short by a loud cry that came from the rear of the house and the Guv strode towards a side alleyway, where he almost collided with two firemen as they ran out. He listened to their breathless report and refused to believe it. 'Where at the back do you say? Over the wall?' The two firemen nodded in urgent unison. By this time, the remaining firemen had searched their respective areas of the street and reported that the call appeared to be a malicious one.

The Station Officer, having hastened down the side alleyway, came across a brick wall about 7 feet high which enclosed a yard behind the street frontage. He climbed onto a convenient ledge and peered head and shoulders over the wall, hoping to find what had struck fear into two of his stalwart men. And there it was – a large lioness, prowling agitatedly around the open space inside the wall. The animal appeared big enough to scale the walls of its prison in one clean jump. The officer stumbled down off his perch and retreated to comparative safety, as the angry lioness displayed a fine set of shining teeth to the strangely clad mortal.

The owner was still locked inside the house, reluctant to meet the police officers who had also arrived. The woman neighbour watched the goings-on from behind her net curtains and it appeared that the malicious fire call had something to do with the unrest of the local population over the presence of the beast in the back garden of the house. After the crews returned to the station, there was talk that the lioness had been seen sitting alongside its owner in his car. There was also a suggestion that he had other 'pets' around the district.

In the light of recent national publicity about the 'pet' lion cult, it is clear that such animals could be a hazard to firemen. What would happen if an animal like this one was tormented by smoke, even from a minor rubbish fire? What would be the outcome of a firework tossed over this particular wall around 5 November? There would be a real possibility of a wild animal at large in Central London. For years we have coped with the dangers of guard dogs on unattended building sites at night, but lions in back gardens!

8

On the Lighter Side

In the course of his work, a fireman witnesses death, injury and suffering at very close quarters. Whenever possible he alleviates sad, sometimes harrowing, sights by smiling at those incidents which do occasionally have a funnier side. Indeed, a fireman's sense of humour is constantly broadened and developed by happenings in which he himself is involved. There was for instance, the case of the old tramp one early winter's morning.

Fire had struck another large London hotel, just off the Bayswater Road, and firemen from the West End and the surrounding divisions had cursed and sweated together towards another victory. Once the fire was surrounded and finally brought under control, the first clearing-up tasks began as relief appliances and their fresh crews arrived. The weary and grime-besmirched men who had fought the fire from the earliest stages handed over their positions and tasks to the newcomers and then, crew by crew, made their way out of the still-smoky steamy hotel into the cold, fresh early-morning air.

Fifty yards up the road from the hotel and tucked in amongst the lines of parked fire appliances was the Brigade's canteen van. Over its roof hung a faint heat-haze as its fireman crew prepared to dispense hot drinks and biscuits to the hundred-odd fire-fighters at the scene. Gradually, the tired crews gathered in a haphazard queue at the serving-hatch, jostling for position and eager to wrap their chilled hands around a warm cup of strong, sweet tea. Once served, the firemen gathered in little groups, some standing, some sitting on the front steps of other hotels, some squatting yoga-fashion on the pavement. The canteen-van crew, having satiated the first thirsty demands, refilled the teapots for the second wave. Gradually the fire-fighters relaxed from the tensions of the past hours. It became a reunion, the air resounding with banter and repartee as crew met crew and old acquaintances were renewed. Cigarettes were rolled, pipes lit, and all appeared well in the world though recent dangers were not forgotten as men from adjacent fire stations talked about the hotel blaze in which *they* had sweated harder than anyone else and exchanged coarse remarks about the conditions down in the basement. One probationer fireman perched alone on a front-doorstep watched the wisps of steam from the hot drink clasped in his shaking hands. Half an hour ago, a ceiling had crashed down over him and two of his mates as they worked a hose-line through a charred corridor – his tea tasted especially good.

By the dim light of the canteen-van serving-hatch, the shadowy figure of an old man watched the animated scene from a nearby doorway. A 'down and out', he had been wandering the streets when the fire had originally broken out. He had watched the first appliances arrive, seen the dramatic ladder rescues, and witnessed the first breathing-apparatus crews going in with hose-lines as the ominous black smoke pouring from the upper floors of the hotel became angrily tinted with orange flame. The old man had been transfixed by all the action, the dashing around, the excitement. Then he had noticed the arrival of the canteen van and the crews gathering round. He edged nearer, doorway by doorway, longing for a sip of tea but inwardly realising that this was an exclusive party.

Amid the throng of firemen, the shaken young probationer, fetching his second cup of tea, noticed the old tramp trying to attract his gaze. Instinctively the fireman held out the tea and hesitatingly, the tramp took it in his hands. Noisily slurping from the cup, he spilled tea down his tattered overcoat. He noticed several other firemen nearby raise their cups and smile at him. The young fireman returned with his own tea and a small packet of biscuits for the old man. 'Ta, son. Were you in that lot back there just now? Reckons you lads earns your keep, I really does. Specially now!'

As dawn began its inexorable lift over London, the re-freshed crews dragged life into their aching limbs and headed off for a hot shower and breakfast back at their stations. On the pavement around the canteen van lay stains from spilt drinks, biscuit crumbs and cigarette dog-ends. The serving-hatch was still up, the lights still on and the counter strewn with empty cups as its crew busied themselves with clearing-up. One after another the last appliances drove away from the scene. Each departure was watched by a solitary figure huddled in a doorway and as the canteen van drew past him, the old tramp raised his hand in salute to the firemen in whose company he had enjoyed such unexpected refreshment.

Another, lighter incident, this time involving children, followed a fire call to a large West London council estate area not long after I had taken command as Station Officer of a busy four-appliance fire station.

Kids, they say, will always be kids, and whenever we turned out to this estate hordes of children watched us. On one such occasion, just after a change of watch, the PE, P and TL arrived at a tower block to find two derelict cars burning fiercely inside a semi-underground car park. There was much smoke and many pointed fingers as the appliances swung into the approach road; there was the inevitable audience of about a hundred kids awaiting the free display.

Hose-lines were quickly laid out and crews in breathing-apparatus penetrated the choking gloom of the basement, located the burning cars and soon had cooling jets to work. Above them, high in the tower block, other firemen checked the situation there and, within minutes, the appliance radio was crackling with another 'stop' message. It was always at about this time that the kids advanced, for with most of the firemen deployed and appliances solely defended by their drivers, the children's sheer weight of numbers easily over-whelmed the men. Generally the kids were well-intentioned;

there was hose to jump on, lovely big escape-ladder wheels to spin, and an inviting world inside the rear cab of the appliance to gaze at through a half-open door. For the more adventurous types, however, remote and unguarded some distance up the street at the hydrant end of the hoses, were the shiny metal key and bar that lifted out so easily.

On this occasion the fire had been put out, and the crews were trying to make up the gear along with the 'help' of these kids – and were without doubt losing. At the peak of frustration, observing one of my recruit firemen as he succumbed to superior forces, I yelled out his Christian name. It was unfortunate that this callow youth's first name had stuck in my mind; it was the sort of name expected of an American folk singer from the deep guitar-pluckin' south. He obviously didn't hear me, so I bellowed out his name again even louder. Eventually he extricated himself from the juvenile mêlée and I deployed him elsewhere in a concerted effort to get all our gear put back on the appliances. It was only then that I realised the kids were chanting his name in football-crowd fashion: 'LEEroy ... LEEroy ... LEEroy', in imitation of my previous yelling. As the pitch of the chanting grew louder, the owner of the unusual name grew redder and redder.

Eventually we managed to pile the last of our hose on board and get under way, accompanied by a convoy of kids on bikes and foot, lookouts posted to watch for young horrors trying to emulate Tarzan on the back of the appliances. This brush with the kids was soon forgotten until another call the next night took us back to the same tower block, this time to a 'person shut in a lift'. As we drew up at the flats there were the kids, and the chanting grew and grew: 'LEEroy ... LEEroy ... LEEroy'. Leeroy himself cringed under the brim of his helmet and tried not to be recognised.

Every kid in the entire estate soon knew the catchy name of one of those firemen who came their way so often. Moreover, and somewhat reluctantly, this young fireman was appointed our 'child welfare officer' and had to try on subsequent calls to this area to cope with his youthful fans. He attempted to keep them from under the feet of the working crews, endeavoured to answer their questions and generally aimed to bring some form of order to the horde. Surprisingly for a young man, he succeeded with the children, even if at times the chanting was a pain in the ears. Indeed, if 'King Leeroy' told them to keep off the escape wheels, they really did take notice.

In fact it was an object lesson to us that instead of fighting the kids, we should try some controlled involvement to make our job a little easier. The kids made Leeroy a bit of a local hero but they could not understand his absence when he was on leave. Then the juvenile natives tended to get a little restless, and we had a terrible job explaining.

A church might not seem to be an appropriate place for a light-hearted incident but the following story shows that it can be. Duties over Christmas naturally keep some firemen away from their wives and families for part of the time, and during such a shift firemen answered a fire call shortly after midnight on Christmas morning to a church just off London's Edgware Road. Upon their arrival outside the church, the crews heard the service in progress within. The Guv despatched some of his men round to the rear of the building and then gingerly and reverently opened the great oak door, took off his fire-helmet and went inside, leaving the remainder of the firemen in the porchway.

The congregation, heads bowed, deep in worship, were quite unaware of the approach of the fire officer; suddenly, as he walked slowly towards the centre aisle, his gaze was caught by a priest standing to one side ahead of him. The priest pointed towards a side aisle on the far side and, as prayers ended, he met the Station Officer and led him to a small nativity display with a barn and the attendant animals. The back of the display was scorched and blackened, and around it on the floor lay a small pool of water. The congregation started to sing the carol 'It Came Upon A Midnight Clear' and, as the melodious strains filled the church, the priest quietly explained to the fire officer what had happened.

An exposed light bulb within the display had fallen on to

some paper material which had slowly overheated and then suddenly flared up, just as the midnight service was about to start. Showing great presence of mind, the priest had unplugged the whole display and gone quickly to the nearest water supply, which happened to be the font almost alongside. He had scooped up a container of water, poured it over the back of the display and then hastened off to call the Brigade.

The Guv made a discreet inspection of the nativity and its surrounding area and, satisfied, turned and retraced his way up the side aisle towards the main door, accompanied by the priest. At the door the fire officer paused and turned to look back towards the officiating clergyman, now in the pulpit ready to deliver his Christmas sermon. Their eyes met and each bowed imperceptibly in respect of the other's calling.

Then the Guv eased open the heavy door and the cold night air flowed into the church. The fire-fighting priest held out his hand. 'We shall remember you in our prayers'. The fire officer mumbled his somewhat embarrassed thanks and the two men shook hands vigorously. The Station Officer then stepped outside into the porch where most of the waiting firemen were gathered. 'Send a stop message. You're not going to believe this.' The burly figure of the Sub approached. 'Find anything, Guv?' 'Oh, yes,' was the Station Officer's reply as the two men walked across the church forecourt. 'I found it all right – it was only a small fire and they put it out before we got here – with what you might call the resources of religion and half-a-gallon of holy water.'

9
Hazards Old and New

Fire damage in 1976 cost £232 million – a figure which continues to spiral year by year, despite the increasing effort on the part of Fire Brigades to make the public more fire-conscious. This appallingly high annual loss represents only direct fire damage, that which the insurance companies can measure. The real fire-loss figure takes account of lost jobs, orders and future contracts, production delays and many other intangibles, and is estimated to be three or four times the actual direct-loss figure.

And what of fire fatalities? In the London area alone in 1976, 128 men, women and children perished, although this awful total could have been far worse. During that year, London firemen rescued 464 adults and children trapped by fire or overcome by smoke from the very face of death.

Firemen everywhere who share in the mammoth task of reducing fire deaths, injuries and material damage know that the vast majority of fires arise from acts of sheer carelessness, discarded cigarettes and match-ends, children playing with matches and faulty electrical wiring being the principal causes. After only a short time in the Brigade, a fireman becomes a connoisseur of human tragedy and misfortune. It may be the aftermath of a gas leak sought out with a lighted match, an oft-blown fuse replaced with a safety pin to keep a circuit working, or the late-night viewer who forgets to pull out his television plug when he turns in. Occasionally there will be a 'classic' example of human folly like the old couple who, feeling cold in bed, placed a lighted paraffin lamp underneath the bed to help keep them warm. Little did they expect such rapid results.

Death and injuries aside, firemen fight a constant crusade to save property and precious contents, be they an expensive computer in an office suite or a widow's pension-book in a smoke-filled bedroom in a back-street terrace. The firemen will offer gentle sympathy to the shocked and sometimes grieving occupier of a fire-damaged building, but inwardly have to view the blackened devastation with equanimity.

A newly joined fireman also gradually becomes aware of a distinct lack of understanding of his role by the general public. In some people's eyes, the Fire Brigade only seems an additional burden to the poor ratepayers. Indeed, unless anyone has cause to dial 999 for the Brigade, he will have little contact with the men in the dashing red appliances. And of course most of us never think that it can happen to us. Hence the vicious circle is complete. I recently met a man who delayed calling the Brigade to his home because he thought he would incur a charge. He dithered until the smoke from his kitchen grew so dense that he was forced to dial 999, by which time the small fire had taken hold of the ground floor of the house. Fortunately, when the first crews arrived and plunged into the smoking mass, they were able to contain the fire to the ground floor, although smoke ruined almost everything upstairs.

It is also sad that in the mid-1970s very few people are aware of the fireman's role in the increasing science of fire prevention. Specialist staff dealing with this aspect inspect plans of new buildings and those being altered to ensure that escape routes, doors, emergency lighting and fire alarms are correctly sited and in accordance with the wealth of safety legislation that the Brigade is charged with applying. Once building work is started, the fire-prevention department monitor its progress. In the course of a year, they also make many thousands of visits to work, leisure and entertainment premises to check that every fire-safety feature is correctly installed and maintained; in some of this work the fire-prevention staff are assisted by operational firemen.

A fast-increasing hazard facing firemen is the leakage and spillage of chemicals, in transit or in storage. Far more tankers are travelling the roads, their loads ranging from the most innocuous liquids such as milk to the toxic, corrosive and flammable solids, liquids and gases used in ever-growing quantities in industry.

When involved in a accident a tanker occasionally ruptures and leaks, and if a hazardous cargo spills out it can cause untold problems for the firemen who have to cope with it. Initially they must urgently identify the substance and what has to be done to render the leakage safe. Is the chemical explosive? Is it highly poisonous? Can we allow it to run down into the drains? Are the fumes dangerous? Should we wear protective clothing and breathing-apparatus? Must the entire area be evacuated? Even if a tanker has not crashed but is merely leaking, all this information is urgently required in the first minutes of the fire-crew's arrival.

Over the last two decades some progress has been made by the chemical industry in the basic marking of substances conveyed by tanker, together with a specialist-advice telephone number for use in event of an emergency. However, this call-service was no great help to firemen trying to cope with a leakage of an unknown and possibly lethal chemical in the early stages of an incident. Indeed, a long-distance telephone call at one o'clock in the morning is a time-consuming exercise and hardly one that endeared the tanker-haulage firms to firemen. As often as not the tanker driver himself didn't know what his load was, let alone its dangers; he only knew he had over 5,000 gallons of it. Firemen used to getting stuck into an emergency incident immediately they arrived found that they were delayed by the problems of tanker loads at road-traffic accidents, especially where people were trapped in wreckage, as has happened in some motorway multiple pile-ups of recent years. The problem of chemical identification and the correct method of 'making safe' thus became vitally important to firemen throughout the UK.

The LFB in fact had for some years been developing its

own code of chemical marking, designed to tell a fireman all he initially needs to know before tackling a chemical situation. The 'Hazchem' code, as it is known, consists of a brief cross-reference of numbers and letters. When applied to any particular hazardous substance and displayed prominently on a tanker or lorry, it enables firemen to tell at a glance whether they can apply copious supplies of water, water spray, foam or a dry powder to the spillage and informs them what personal protection they must wear while working near the leak.

When correctly applied, the Hazchem code obviously saves valuable time and the need for every fireman to be weighed down under a pile of chemical textbooks. It has been adopted by most of the emergency services in the country, but can only work efficiently if all hazardous cargoes are marked with it. The chemical industry generally is aware of the problems that some of its products create for Fire Brigades and, in some cases, firms have developed their own 'back-up' specialist teams to assist firemen at incidents involving their own tankers. Sadly, however, there are still many dangerous unmarked cargoes thundering the motorways and threading through the busy high streets up and down the land.

For several years now, following the growing problem in London as reflected in the steady increase in the number of chemical incidents, a qualified chemist on call twenty-four hours a day has been sent to every such emergency to give direct advice to the fire crews at the scene. In addition, a special HQ Control Unit has been commissioned which comes into action at the same time as the local station appliances and acts as a mobile focal point at the incident, its staff providing 'de-contamination' equipment should it be required.

Tankers are not the only chemical hazard. Spillages, leakages and fires increasingly often involve chemicals of one sort

(*Opposite*)
Firemen wearing full protective suits and compressed-air BA sets undergo decontamination after making safe a lorry-load of leaking containers of corrosive chemicals; 1978 (*Owen Rowland*)

or another inside industrial premises, laboratories and teaching establishments, and a fireman's role is given an added dimension of danger. During 1976 in the LFB area alone, there were 136 spillages or leaks of chemicals and 29 fires directly involving a chemical substance. In the course of their work at these calls, 137 firemen required hospital treatment, and of these 14 were detained. The undoubted danger to the general public at such emergency calls rarely receives the publicity it deserves, possibly because to date there has been no major loss of life, except at the Flixborough disaster which resulted from a fault within the chemical plant itself.

There was, however, the tragic case of a woman motorist involved in a multiple pile-up in fog on the M6 several years ago. Her car was trapped between two heavy lorries; one of them was a tanker containing acid and in the impact of the crash its tank had ruptured, spilling out the contents. The woman struggled out of her car and splashed her way through the acid flowing around, unaware of its deadly nature. The driver of the tanker made a brave effort to stop her running further into the liquid, but by this time the poor woman had collapsed into the acid, overcome by the powerful fumes, and died an excruciatingly horrible death. Because she was only one of many who died in the crash, the particular circumstances of her death made little impact on the media or the public.

This was not the case quite recently when a laden petrol tanker skidded, overturned and caught fire in a pretty South Midlands village early one morning. The fierce conflagration destroyed the tanker and a considerable part of the village centre before battling firemen controlled and subdued the flowing and blazing petrol. 'Ban the tankers from minor roads' went up the cry and, although no life was lost in this particular instance, had the tanker been carrying toxic chemicals the consequences for the sleeping villagers could possibly have been far worse. A cloud of poisonous gas could have enveloped them in a cloak of silence.

Occasionally, not all 'chemical incidents' turn out to be so.

One Central London fire station responded to an emergency call to 'chemicals fallen off lorry', and on arrival the firemen found two 45 gallon metal drums lying damaged in the road, spewing out a suspicious-looking thick red liquid. They quickly cordoned off the area and stopped motorists and pedestrians who were driving and walking through the sticky mass. The drums bore no markings and the driver of the lorry had no idea what they contained. A full-scale operation was therefore started by firemen in full protective suits and breathing-apparatus to prevent the liquid running into the drains nearby, and London's rush-hour traffic ground to a halt. After an hour of uncertainty, phone calls and a close look by the Brigade's chemist, the liquid was discovered to be a soya-bean extract and absolutely harmless! If the drums had been marked, everyone would have been saved a lot of time, effort and frustration.

Another occasion illustrates just how easily chemical accidents occur and endanger the firemen who are called to sort out the aftermath. This incident, like the previous one, took place in a Central London street during the rush hour. Dustmen making their routine calls to shop and office premises had collected several bottles, drums, rubbish cartons and other paper packages from a recently vacated building, and all these items were tossed into the dustcart and pushed forward by a compressing device. Unknown to the dustmen, the empty premises had last housed an industrial chemist and, as a second load of boxes was thrown into the dustcart, a loud explosion from within the cart knocked a nearby dustman flat on his face, started a fire inside the vehicle and rattled all the windows down the street. The fire was still burning when the Brigade arrived several minutes later and the injured dustman was speedily removed to hospital.

The firemen found that amongst the boxes inside the dustcart were many containing assorted chemicals which had interacted to produce an explosive cocktail. The fire call quickly became a 'chemical' incident. Police evacuated the street whilst firemen in protective clothing and BA climbed into the

115

cart and started to unload and sift through the five tons of refuse already collected, for signs of any more 'lethal' rubbish. This unpleasant task was directed by the Brigade's chemist who was now at the scene, and a full decontamination area was set up ready to deal with any fireman who made contact with any suspect substance. After four hours of painstaking and gentle digging by over fifty firemen in relays, all the many containers and packages of discarded chemicals were recovered, many intact, and the incident was finally closed.

It was fortunate that at the time the explosion took place in the crowded street only one person, the innocent dustman, was injured. But it was unfortunate that the London *Evening News* chose to report the incident, its potential danger, and the sweat and toil of the firemen as a 'bomb scare'. Had the newspaper reported the facts in depth, it would have done more to underline the Brigade's ever-growing workload at such incidents and the undoubted risks that confront firemen at chemical situations throughout the length and breadth of the kingdom.

Outside such emergency calls, operational firemen have many activities to occupy their time. They maintain all the equipment carried on appliances, from sophisticated breathing equipment down to the well-provided first-aid boxes. They take part in daily physical-training exercises in order to keep active and alert. There are strenuous drill sessions, full-scale exercises to improve techniques in handling ladders and other fire-fighting gear, and regular lectures on all manner of relevant technical subjects. Besides all this, there are hundreds of street fire-hydrants to be inspected, together with visits to the many varied buildings that would pose a particular threat if involved in fire.

As part of their training for promotion, junior officers from the rank of Leading Fireman onwards attend residential courses at one of the two Home Office fire colleges. At the newer of these, at Moreton-in-Marsh in Gloucestershire, are what must be the finest and most modern facilities in the world for creating real fire situations. Amongst the purpose-built buildings on the 'fireground' of this college are a multi-storey industrial block, a high-rise block, an electrical sub-station and a domestic property. There is also the whole centre section of a large cargo ship (constructed in concrete) and several types of oil tank, one as large as those found in oil refineries. All these buildings and constructions can be 'fired' and all produce vivid real-life conditions for the junior-officer students to tackle. Additional facilities simulate underground sewer rescues, lift accidents and road crashes involving hazardous chemicals. The college also has comprehensive heat, smoke and humidity 'torture chambers' for those Brigade officers who aspire to become instructors in their own Brigades, and these BA courses are the most physically demanding of all.

Both colleges run intensive fire-prevention and general-management courses for junior, middle and senior levels of officers and the whole collective training effort's ultimate aim is to develop the know-how and ability of the modern-day Fire Brigade and its personnel.

The public hardly ever seem to appreciate this background to Fire Service work, often thinking of a fireman as being a plebian squirter of water, instead of the highly trained, around-the-clock rescue and emergency expert he really is. Indeed, a frequent gibe often heard by crews who have turned out to the scene of a 999 call is, 'I bet this has disturbed your snooker!' or 'Sorry about your game of cards!' Both are guaranteed to make even the most reticent fireman flush.

Happily there are many occasions when a person whose business or home has suffered fire damage wants to express his gratitude to the firemen concerned. Hardly a week passes without letters of thanks and the occasional cheque for the Brigade Welfare or National Fire Service Benevolent funds arriving at Brigade headquarters at Lambeth.

After years as a 'silent service', the London Fire Brigade has now got to its feet and is banging the public-relations drum loud and clear. It has recently taken peak-viewing-hour television time to spell out fire dangers; it gives talks to more adult groups and has more visitors to its fire stations every year.

At child level, the Brigade runs more 'firemanship' courses and Duke of Edinburgh award schemes than ever before.

Hopefully, this growing educational aspect will go some way towards arresting the horrific fire deaths and soaring losses of each subsequent year, and perhaps bring about a reduction in the number of tragic scenes a fireman acts out as part of his profession. As you can see, like the famous policeman in Gilbert and Sullivan, a fireman's lot is not (always) a happy one.

10

Great Fires and Firemen Past

Organised fire-fighting in London has its origins in the Roman occupation, where fire-fighters known as *vigiles* stood by with ladders, axes and buckets, although not organised on the scale of ancient Rome. Early attempts were made in the eleventh century to restrict fires lit in the open, and lights had to be extinguished at nightfall. Fire was obviously feared but not in any positive way controlled. In the first Great Fire of London in 1212, over 3,000 people are said to have perished and houses on London Bridge were amongst the property burned to the ground.

Still there was no organised attempt at fire-fighting and in 1561 the steeple of Old St Paul's was destroyed, despite a heroic attempt by the Lord Mayor to discipline the band of helpers. Some suggested making a fire-break by demolishing part of the cathedral roof, others wanted to shoot down the burning steeple with cannon fire. Alas, the Lord Mayor's efforts at some semblance of organisation failed and the steeple collapsed above the fire-fighters as they argued amongst themselves.

Even at the beginning of the seventeenth century, no great improvements had been made in London's fire-fighting manpower although by this time the first crude water mains were in use and hand-held water squirts first appeared, larger ones being mounted on wheels. 'Firemen' were still drawn from the ill-disciplined crowd of bystanders. The Great Fire of 1666 saw a total loss of £10 million as 84 churches, 44 livery halls and 13,000 dwellings were razed to the ground. Surprisingly, it claimed only six lives. In 1667 came new fire-safety regulations, dividing the city into four areas, each equipped with 800 buckets, 50 ladders, pickaxes and shovels.

Large and damaging fires still broke out, however, and insurance companies who for some time had been insuring mercantile risks started to sell policies that covered buildings against fire damage. The insurance companies recruited their own Brigades, often using men from the Thames barges and floats, and equipped them with manually pumped appliances. These early firemen followed their own occupations until summoned by messenger to a fire, not unlike today's rural county 'retained' firemen called out by siren or 'bleeper'. The insurance-company firemen were drilled in the use of their appliances and paid well for their attendances at both drills and fires. They wore resplendent uniform coats and hats and proudly displayed the badges of their respective companies. There was much rivalry between Brigades. Indeed, there are instances in the early eighteenth century where the first Brigade to arrive at a fire would look on unconcerned as the flames grew higher if the building was not insured with them. When the appropriate Brigade did arrive, the rival firemen would impede their efforts to put out the inferno.

However, insurance companies and Brigades soon saw the futility of this and began to vie amongst themselves to provide the most efficient and speediest service. With a growing fire-awareness came more powerful manual pumps, although in the outer London areas and in the country only smaller parish pumps were provided manned solely by volunteers. These men were normally paid for their attendance at fires in vast quantities of ale, and when the barrels dried up so did the pumping.

By 1824, London surprisingly still lacked a unified Fire Brigade, although one was already in existence in Edinburgh. In 1832, the insurance companies in London at last decided to amalgamate their resources into one body – the London Fire

Engine Establishment – and the Edinburgh fire chief, James Braidwood, was put in command. Eighty full-time professional firemen were employed on a continuous-duty system at nineteen fire stations. Initially, they attended about three fires a day in the capital.

Over the next twenty-five years, Braidwood built up the LFEE into an effective fire-fighting force, although it was still not municipally supported. As the fire risks of London grew – its dense population, slums, docks and warehouses constantly multiplying – so the services of the LFEE continued to be in demand. Queen Victoria, unimpressed with the efforts of local volunteer firemen dealing with a fire in Windsor Castle, bade Braidwood and his Brigade attend and a special train rushed him and a contingent of his men to the scene.

Sadly, Braidwood was killed by a falling wall at a massive fire at a Tooley Street warehouse in 1861. His funeral procession was a mile and a half long, and as it filed through the city streets en route to the cemetery, every church tolled a single bell in memory and respect of London's first Fire Chief. Following the tragedy, a government select committee was formed to look into the problem of developing a London Brigade that would be able to keep pace with the fire hazards of the rapidly growing capital. The outcome was a recommendation for a municipally controlled Brigade on an establishment scheme approved by the Home Secretary.

In the meantime, the insurance companies were still anxious to replace Braidwood, and their choice fell upon Captain Eyre Massey Shaw, a young ex-Irish Army Officer, who was running the Belfast Police and Fire Brigade very successfully at the time. Shaw took up his post in command of the LFEE in 1861. In 1865, Parliament passed an Act to establish a Fire Brigade for the metropolis, and in the same year Massey Shaw became the first Chief Officer of the new Metropolitan Fire Brigade. The new Brigade was administered by the Metropolitan Board of Works, the forerunner of the London County Council. The insurance-financed LFEE fire stations, pumps and personnel became its nucleus.

Massey Shaw quickly made a reputation for being a strict disciplinarian. With his strong and forceful personality he constantly demanded further means from the Board of Works to expand and equip his Brigade to his requirements, and he personally led his firemen into battle at most major London fires, whatever the time of day or night. The men of the Metropolitan Brigade quickly came to respect and admire their new Chief. Under him, the MFB slowly grew with new fire stations, firemen and equipment being commissioned, including the very latest horse-drawn steamer pumps.

The dashing Shaw and his Brigade made an early impression on the young Prince of Wales who had shown a great fascination for organised fire-fighting displays in his childhood. His involvement in the early years of the MFB reached such a pitch that he went to fires himself, either with the firemen on their steamer from Chandos Street Fire Station near Charing Cross, where he had his own fire-uniform kept, or when Massey Shaw sent a carriage to collect him from Clarence House. These activities were not widely known for it was relatively easy for the prince in his brass helmet and fire-uniform to blend into the many activities at a fire, quite unrecognised except by the men of the Metropolitan Brigade. When the future king arrived at a major fire, word went round the firemen pretty quickly.

A particularly spectacular fire that the Prince of Wales attended broke out in the late evening of 7 December 1882, in the auditorium of the Alhambra Theatre in London's Leicester Square, not long after the audience had left. The dramatised version of this unusual story runs as follows.

Massey Shaw sent Superintendent Hamlyn in a carriage to fetch the prince and Shaw himself as he stood surveying the burning theatre, tall, slim in resplendent uniform, hands on hips, grey goatee beard under his helmet, looked every inch the 'Fire King' of the capital, as he had come to be called.

At the scene of the blaze, burly firemen hurried past their

Chief. The air was heavy with thick black smoke punching out of the theatre doors and openings. A dimly visible orange glow of pent-up fire flickered insistently high up over the roof. Superintendent Palmer hurried up to report to Massey Shaw: 'All crews are now withdrawn from within, sir, and I fear for the surrounding premises.' Palmer's face was blackened with grimy sweat and the veins in his neck stood out in sharp relief. 'Very good, Palmer, I'm taking charge. And Palmer, His Royal Highness is on his way.'

Two steamer pumps, their horses foam-flecked, the brass-helmeted crews clinging to the sides, swung into the square and added to the mêlée of fire, smoke and sound. On the far side several policemen struggled to keep back the swelling crowd of curious and agitated onlookers. A fireman moved along the feet of the crowd, uncoiling more hose to join the tangled mass already swamping Leicester Square.

En route to the fire, the Prince of Wales and Hamlyn sat shoulder to shoulder in the brougham, faced by Major Stranks, the prince's equerry. Both the prince and Hamlyn were bearded and of portly build, although the prince at forty-one was the younger. They each wore identical fire-uniforms – brass-buttoned tunics, leather belts and axes, and brass helmets. Stranks, a much slighter man in the plumed hat and uniform of an officer of Hussars, had hardly enough room to get his highly polished boots amongst those of the two firemen squeezed into the carriage opposite him. Stranks always felt uncomfortable on these occasions – the brougham was going far too fast and Stranks never did enjoy going to fires.

Upon their arrival at the fire, Massey Shaw briefly met the Prince of Wales and then left him in the care of Hamlyn who, having collected the prince, usually accompanied him throughout the fire-fighting foray and was thus responsible for his safety, though often he had a job to prevent the royal fireman becoming too involved in fire-fighting operations, frequently in situations of some danger. By this time a desperate battle to save the surrounding buildings encircling the doomed theatre was under way. 'Come on Superintendent. I want to get up to those jets on that roof – should get a good view from there. Come on!' And Hamlyn obediently followed the helmeted figure of the Prince of Wales up the stairs of an adjacent building and along a flat roof, from where part of the fire was being fought.

The prince reached the crouching crew on the roof as they were playing two powerful jets onto the raging fire below. 'Now then, what's going on here?' 'We're doing well 'ere, your 'ighness, and 'itting a lot of fire.' Suddenly thick clouds of acrid smoke drifted back over them as the wind veered. 'Well, keep your heads down, and keep up the good work!' As the smoke cleared momentarily, Hamlyn asked the firemen what was going on further down a catwalk. With his brass helmet gleaming as flames from the theatre opposite broke out furthet through the roof, the fireman replied that it was a crew from Chandos Street working a couple of jets in a courtyard.

At the front of the Alhambra, in Leicester Square, Massey Shaw turned to the Superintendent at his side and snapped, 'We're still losing it, Palmer.' In the background, steamer pumps, their flywheels and valve gear lost in a blur of motion, rocked gently upon their wheels. Incandescent sparks cascaded up from the steamer chimneys high over the square as grimy firemen-engineers tended their machines. Lines of hose led away from the pumps in all directions.

Massey Shaw shouted for more covering jets: 'At least three more on each side, do your hear! Those premises *must* be held.' And Palmer hurried off.

Hovering beside Massey Shaw stood the Prince of Wales' equerry who had, as usual, elected to stay clean, dry and out of danger at the control point. With some urgency Massey Shaw asked him if he had seen the prince recently. 'Not since we first arrived, sir. He went off with Superintendent Hamlyn.' The Chief Officer's anxious impatience showed: 'I wish he would stay at the front! This fire is going all ways.'

The fire in the theatre was now indeed spreading across gaps and alleyways to several adjoining buildings and, despite the valiant efforts of 200 firemen and their 20 steamer pumping-

appliances, many offices, shops and clubs on either side of the
original fire were now part of it. In the narrow, gas-lit, cobbled
courtyard on one side of the inferno, the Prince of Wales and
Superintendent Hamlyn found their position increasingly un-
tenable. Heat from intense flames very close at hand added to
the discomfort of swirling smoke and flying sparks. Water from
the many jets attacking the fire flowed in torrents down the
gutters and the yellow globes of the gas-lights were sporadically
cloaked in smoke. But the royal heir appeared to be unmoved,
and struggled to assist a toiling crew of firemen reposition a jet
further down the courtyard.

Water flowed around their boots and a fine spray from the
hose-nozzle blew back over their parched faces. Suddenly, a
gasping, sweating fireman appeared and reported that their
path back to safety was threatened by flames. Hamlyn shouted,
'Leave the jets – and quickly!' He and the prince led the group
of firemen away down the courtyard; as they did so, part of the
gable-end of the theatre roof above broke loose, swayed and
then fell with an explosive roar into the blazing interior. A
whirlwind of sparks rose into the night sky and tons of red-hot
stone and brickwork crashed into the courtyard below, directly
in the path of the retreating line of men.

News of the collapse in the courtyard reached Massey Shaw
at the Control point, the message being that several men were
trapped including the Prince of Wales. Shaw quickly reached
the scene and through the smoke, lit by the fire-glow from
above, the bulky figure of the prince appeared in the midst of
the chaos. Lifting beams of timber, passing bricks and lumps of
broken stone along the human chain, the Prince of Wales
toiled alongside the firemen. Massey Shaw could do no more –
rescue for the buried men was under way and he had to return
to his post at the front of the fire. Messengers would keep him
informed of progress; the blaze had yet to be contained.

The trapped firemen, one of whom was Superintendent
Hamlyn, once released were speedily removed to hospital. The
prince then rejoined Massey Shaw in the square and stayed
until after 4am, when it was clear that the fire had finally been

surrounded and was under control. By this time, the Alhambra Theatre was a charred, smoking and partially collapsed ruin.

That same morning, *The Times* carried a very detailed story of the Alhambra fire in its later editions, telling of the battle to save the theatre and of the injuries to seven of Massey Shaw's fire-fighters. Of the Prince of Wales's involvement *The Times* said nothing – a point noticed by the prince, as clad in a velvet dressing-gown in the clean air of Clarence House, he enjoyed his breakfast coffee and cigar over the newspaper account of the fire. The prince's reverie was suddenly broken by his equerry, who entered the breakfast room and proffered an envelope on a silver tray. Major Stranks looked weary. 'From Captain Eyre Massey Shaw, your Highness.'

The Prince of Wales reached for his paper knife, exposing the lint dressings on both hands and wrists. The letter read: 'Assistant-Officer Ashford and Firemen Fourth-class Chatterton and Berg, all suffering head and body injuries, burns and cuts. Superintendent Hamlyn suffering broken arm and burns. Three others with cuts and burns: Charing Cross Hospital. Ashford, Chatterton and Berg expected to be detained some time. Your obedient servant, Eyre Massey Shaw.' The Prince of Wales paused, drew on his cigar and looked up. 'My carriage Stranks, in one hour, for the Charing Cross Hospital. Send word for Massey Shaw to meet me there. And have seven boxes of my cigars made up for the men.'

The equerry left the room to organise the morning ahead, whilst the prince returned to *The Times*' account of the fire. He stood up, stretched his aching back and went into his bedroom. His fire-uniform had long since been removed but the unmistakable pungent aroma of smoke and fire clung to the royal bedroom furnishings.

The foregoing account of the Alhambra fire is a dramatised version. A documented eye-witness account shows that the prince really was at the scene from the very early stages of operations, unrecognised by the vast crowd of late-night theatre-goer spectators. It is not at all improbable that he was near to where the collapse took place and took some part in the rescue of those trapped by the fall.

Later on that morning, and accompanied by Massey Shaw, the Prince of Wales did visit the seven injured men in Charing Cross Hospital and presented each with a large box of cigars. Sadly, two of the injured, Assistant-Officer Ashford and Fire-man Berg, both died later that same day, but all the others subsequently recovered and returned to fire-fighting duties. *The Times* duly recorded the prince's visit with Massey Shaw to the hospital during the morning of 7 December 1882. From Charing Cross, he went on with Shaw to view the remains of the Alhambra and this visit, according to that newspaper, was his first! Today the Odeon Cinema stands upon the site of the Alhambra Theatre and there is nothing to record the dramatic night of ninety-six years ago when the heir to the throne joined the 'Fire King' at the scene of one of London's worst-ever theatre fires.

Massey Shaw socialised with the Prince of Wales over many years and at one stage was summoned by the queen to advise on suitable fire-protection measures for the royal palaces. Amid all this activity, Shaw also found time and energy to write several detailed manuals of fire-fighting which laid down the foundations of modern techniques, and, in 1882, the 'Fire King' was immortalised in Gilbert and Sullivan's *Iolanthe* with the verse:

> Oh, Captain Shaw!
> Type of true love kept under!
> Could thy brigade
> With cold cascade
> Quench my great love I wonder!

In 1891, he resigned after thirty years as London's Fire Chief and was knighted the same year.

By this time, principally through Shaw's efforts and pressure on local and national government, the MFB was probably the most highly organised and trained Fire Brigade in the world. Its firemen however, still worked a continuous-duty system, endured a rigid discipline code and suffered several deaths and frequent injuries every year in the ordinary line of duty.

The twentieth century saw the introduction of the first self-propelled fire appliances, at first steam, then electric and eventually petrol-driven. Equipment also improved apace – canvas fire-hose began to replace leather hose and early attempts to provide a breathing-apparatus set for firemen were made, although at first these were little more than a smoke-hood worn by a fireman inside a smoke-filled building and fed by a flexible pipe from an air-pump outside. Foam was developed for use on petrol and oil fires as the use of the motor car grew, and parliamentary fire-legislation was enacted. This required strict and safe-handling and storage of celluloid, which had complicated fires where many lives had been lost.

In the early 1900s, London firemen gradually became discontented with their duty system and the Spartan conditions under which they worked. However, when World War I broke out, the rumblings of unrest were stifled in the men's patriotic feelings as almost one-quarter of the firemen in the Brigade who were reservists joined the colours.

Early Zeppelin raids over London in 1915 gave the remaining firemen a foretaste of what was to come. Supplemented by volunteers over military age and men from several industrial 'works' Fire Brigades, they faced high-explosive and incendiary bombs which in one night alone caused twenty-nine fires in one small area of the City. Towards the end of the war, such was the bomb and fire damage being inflicted on London that the War Cabinet ordered the recall of all London firemen serving in the armed forces.

At the end of the war, firemen again pursued improvements in hours, pay and conditions and, in December 1918, their newly formed union won one day's leave in ten and a 10s a week pay rise. During the depression years that followed firemen were forced to take a cut in wages. The years between the wars did, however, see a considerable improvement in the technology of fire-fighting and in London the very last horse-drawn fire-appliance, based at Kensington, was withdrawn in 1921. In the thirties the first all-enclosed appliance appeared, providing its crew with some protection from the elements en route to a call and preventing the frequent injuries to firemen thrown off the older appliances, where the crew sat down the sides and tried to rig in fire-gear as the vehicle dashed to the fire scene. A fireman's training, expertise and equipment generally improved; even brass helmets, a traditional part of the uniform since Massey Shaw's day, were replaced by cork helmets as the widespread use of electricity in home and industry created a new hazard to the fire-fighter.

One of London's largest and most spectacular fires of the thirties was the burning of the Crystal Palace on Anerley Hill, South London, on the night of 30 November 1936. This vast showpiece exhibition building was originally constructed in Hyde Park to house the Great Exhibition of 1851 and re-erected on the Anerley Hill site in 1854. The imposing glass, timber and cast-iron framed building became the fire responsibility of the Penge Urban District Council Fire Brigade. The Crystal Palace was about 1,400 feet by 450 feet and at its highest point was 160 feet high. It also had two towers of 250 feet at either end of the main building.

At about 1925 hours, one of the private firemen employed at the Crystal Palace saw a streak of flame run along the top of a room. Quite incredibly, considering the vast risk of the massive building, Penge Fire Brigade were not called until thirty-four minutes later, and when they arrived with their total complement of one motor pumping-appliance and eight firemen a severe fire was raging inside the central glazed transept. Despite being hampered in their efforts by crowds of sightseers and motorists, Penge Fire Brigade managed to attack the spreading inferno with their entire resources, one jet of water.

The Penge firemen soon called for help and the London

The burning of the Crystal Palace, 30 November 1936. Part
of the central transept crashes to the ground (*Daily Sketch*)

Brigade and several smaller ones came to the aid of the totally
overwhelmed local firemen. As the reinforcing pumps arrived
and got to work it was clear that the fire had a considerable
hold over the historic building, for a strong wind was fanning
the flames. Only ten minutes after the Penge crew arrived,
the entire centre transept collapsed in a spectacular and
upwards-spiralling mushroom cloud, throwing up fragments of
burning glass and timber sparks. In the words of one eye-
witness, 'the building began to flame from end to end.'

A huge crowd gathered and hampered the efforts of every
fresh fire appliance which tried to get to the scene. And once
the crews had fought their way through the jostling throng an
insufficient water supply added to the problems. The whole of
the Crystal Palace area was ankle-deep in interwoven fire-
hoses, and within an hour of the arrival of the first Penge

firemen over 70 pumps and other appliances crewed by over 400 fire-fighters were at work.

At this stage the fire could be seen from most of South and Central London and the glow was clearly visible in all the surrounding counties. Among the dignitaries who visited the scene of operations was the Duke of Kent who, accompanied by Major Morris, Chief Officer of the London Fire Brigade, moved through the wind-blown smoke, sparks and spray amongst the crouching firemen.

Slowly and remorselessly, the Crystal Palace which had been a landmark to Londoners for eighty years, twisted and fell to earth. By midnight the inferno had been surrounded on all sides by a barrage of jets and was under control. Fire-fighting carried on all through the night and in the misty first light of dawn, almost the entire 28 acre site was seen to be reduced to thousands of tons of blackened, smouldering piles of twisted ironwork and great solidified sheets of lava-like glass. Only the two towers survived and they appeared even taller as they bore witness to the sad and wholesale destruction below. Whilst no member of the public lost their life in the blaze, several firemen required hospital treatment for cuts and burns.

At the subsequent inquiry it was thought that leaking gas had been the cause of the fire, but clearly the delay of over half an hour between the discovery of a flame and the first alerting of the Fire Brigade allowed the fire to develop unhindered and gain a considerable hold. The fire was also aided by the vast open and unpartitioned areas of the transepts together with a lack of fire-protection equipment such as a sprinkler system. The absence of such fundamental fittings in a vast public building would not be allowed under today's fire and building regulations.

At its second home on Anerley Hill, the Crystal Palace had survived several near-disasters before the ultimate tragedy struck. Even whilst re-erection work was in progress in 1853, a serious collapse of scaffolding killed twelve workmen. The north wing of the Palace suffered severe storm damage in 1861 and this same wing was destroyed by fire five years later, al-

The morning after the Crystal Palace fire. View looking towards the North Tower showing near total destruction (*The Times*)

though on that occasion it appears the local Brigade were successful in containing the outbreak. In 1880, a large elevated water tank burst causing considerable damage.

In its heyday in the late-nineteenth century, the Crystal Palace hosted many exhibitions, concerts, fêtes and the odd firework display; it was visited by royalty from many parts of the world. Even Blondin, the high-wire walker, performed amazing feats on a wire suspended between the ornate glazed panels of the central auditorium. Somewhat ironically, selected contingents of local Fire Brigades were reviewed at the Crystal Palace by the Kaiser in 1891 – no doubt the fire-fighting enthusiasm of the Prince of Wales was behind this enterprise.

The burning of the Crystal Palace brought to an end a building that had a glorious and spectacular history, and London was never again to see the like of such a huge glass, iron and timber structure. The final pyrotechnic display as the Crystal Palace itself blazed is still talked about in local quarters with awe and reverence, as many people recall the drama of that windy and cold November night forty-two years ago.

The start of World War II saw the London Brigade regular firemen ready at their posts, along with 23,000 men and women 'part-timers' of the Auxiliary Fire Service with their 2,000 fire-appliances. After a lull when the expected early air-raids failed to materialise, London suddenly suffered very heavily in August 1940. Over several hours, tons of high-explosive and incendiary bombs rained down from enemy aircraft. Many AFS crews had their first baptism of flame, and major fires raged in the city and in the docks for many hours. On the late afternoon of 7 September came another heavy raid and over 1,000 fire calls were received in the LCC area alone. At one stage the West Ham Brigade, totally overwhelmed by the fire situation in their area, asked London for 500 extra pumps as the skies all around the Royal group of docks glowed with angry and consuming flame.

While civilians sheltered in their homes or deep below the streets in tube railway stations, firemen above worked on, in constant danger from falling bombs, flying shrapnel, collapsing buildings and raging and almost-uncontrolled fire. The bombs frequently shattered street water-mains and firemen had to use what water supplies were at hand. Many raids occurred when the Thames was at low tide, and portable pumps had to be manhandled through thigh-deep mud to provide the badly needed jets of water. At one time St Paul's Cathedral was totally ringed by fire but, by the combined efforts of hundreds of firemen, the historic building was virtually undamaged. Many off-duty crews, both regulars and AFS, reported in and worked selflessly into the dawn. The AFS crews had only one uniform which entailed a quick hang-up to dry out during the daytime lull, ready for the next night's soaking.

From September 1940, London was raided by enemy aircraft for fifty-seven consecutive nights, but with assistance from outside Brigades, London and its firemen survived the onslaught. Whenever possible, London spared contingents of firemen to assist other cities also being hard-hit by raids, and convoys of London crews and appliances travelled to Bristol, Portsmouth, Manchester and other industrial centres. In 1941, the government nationalised all the nation's Fire Services into the National Fire Service, enabling an organisation to be created that could effectively control and administer the fire-fighting resources of the country. At that time, many adjacent Brigades still could not supplement each other's efforts owing to different sized hose-couplings and other incompatible equipment.

From 1944, the coming of the flying bombs and rockets (V1 and V2) saw firemen in London responding to a new menace and providing first-line rescue crews at the scene of devastation where a flying bomb or rocket had fallen. By the end of the war, 327 men and women of the London Region of the NFS had been killed in action. Winston Churchill said of the nation's fire-fighters: 'They are a grand lot and their work must never be forgotten.'

In 1948, Fire Brigades returned to local authority control and many men who had joined the AFS stayed on to make the Fire Service their career. Slowly, as financial restraints allowed, old fire stations were closed, existing ones improved and up-dated. The first diesel-engined appliances were introduced and the first centralised 999 London fire-control centre was opened. In that year also, street fire-alarms started to be abolished as the use of telecommunications grew. More embracing fire prevention and safety requirements were introduced and the Brigade became increasingly involved in these matters.

In 1960, a tragedy of appalling magnitude took place in Glasgow – a city well-used to death and suffering caused by fire. When other cities in the UK were able to demolish slums and develop new areas of housing and industry, Glasgow still had a vast legacy of densely packed dwellings, workshops and warehouses which meant a fire-risk probably second to none. Indeed, men of the Glasgow Fire Brigade boasted that they were the busiest in the world, and it was certainly true that loss of life and incidence of serious outbreak there were far higher than normal.

In the early evening of 28 March 1960, three fire appliances of Glasgow Brigade were called to a fire in a bonded store full of whisky. The six-storey building in Cheapside Street was in an area of narrow, congested streets close by the Clyde, surrounded by other bonded stores and warehouses.

When the first crews arrived at about 1918 hours, there was considerable smoke coming from the bond and great heat within, but no actual fire was showing from the building. Immediate reinforcements were called for and BA crews began to penetrate the smoke-filled floors to locate the hidden fire. Additional hose-jets were laid out ready to protect the surrounding premises should the fire in the whisky bond suddenly break loose.

Then, without any warning, some thirty minutes after the 999 call, came the most deafening explosion from deep inside the building, instantly blowing out the front and rear walls and showering tons of brickwork and debris out into the surrounding streets. Once the clouds of dust had settled, there in side streets stood piles of rubble, some 15 feet high, where fire-fighters and their appliances had been at work only seconds before. The fire in the bond was now unleashed and, fed by many thousands of gallons of whisky, it roared its ferocity at the firemen as the flames reached up high into the night sky. By the light of the inferno, surviving men tore with their bare hands at the piles of rubble under which many fire-fighters were trapped, but it quickly became apparent that no one underneath could still be alive.

More appliances raced to the scene to try to check the advance of the fire which had now spread to two adjoining whisky bonds, a large bottling store nearby and part of the roof of the Clyde shipbuilders, Harland & Wolff. In the latter building, large quantities of liquid air lay stored, and there was a very real danger of a further massive explosion if the fire engulfed any more of those premises. But the battle to contain the blaze was eventually won at about 0130 hours the next morning, by which time over seventy fire-fighting jets were at full blast, including several from a Glasgow Fire Brigade fire-boat out in the Clyde.

The explosion and fire in the whisky bond had devastated the building and it was only after the fire was under control that firemen began the sad task of recovering the bodies of their colleagues. Up to this point the exact number of dead was uncertain, although a roll-call had been undertaken. To everyone's horror when the results of this became known there appeared to be nineteen men 'missing presumed dead'. As the rumour of a disaster spread quickly around the city, the wives and relatives of firemen on duty that evening gathered at the headquarters fire station. As the crowd grew desperate for news, the scene was like that at the head of a mine shaft following a pit accident. No one could be exactly sure how many men were dead and, as the great fire burned on, the anxious groups waited for news that their loved ones were safe. In the near distance, fire-bells from appliances gave urgency to the sad scene.

As dawn rose over the city, and while crews were still at work damping down the smouldering remains of fire, the last of the bodies was recovered from under the rubble. Slowly the scale of the tragedy became clear – the death total stood at 19 men; of these 14 were Glasgow firemen and 5 were members of the city's Salvage Corps. The bodies were so mutilated that identification was only possible through uniform numbers and personal belongings. All the dead men except one were married, and most had young children. Their service ranged from one year to the thirty years of the Deputy Chief Salvage Officer.

That morning the people of Glasgow went to work stunned by the disaster in Cheapside Street. Hundreds of messages of sympathy poured in, including one from the Queen. Later that day Princess Margaret interrupted a civic visit to Glasgow to view the still-smoking remains of the ill-fated whisky bond and the surrounding damage. Even at this early stage, the fire loss was estimated to be around £5 million. The whole country mourned the awful loss of life, a total which still stands today as the worst single tragedy ever to befall the British Fire Service.

The inquiry into the disaster held several months later heard that the cause of the explosion was probably a build-up of whisky vapour that became ignited by flame within the bond itself. The cause of the fire was attributed to either a dropped light (cigarette-end or match) or an electrical fault. Recommendations were made at the hearing that an automatic fire-alarm system should be installed in all bonded warehouses to give an early warning of smoke and fire, and that the siting of such bonds should in future be licensed by local authorities.

Such a massive fire involving a bonded warehouse on the scale of the Cheapside Street blaze has yet to occur in the capital, but London does have a number of such buildings. However, unlike Glasgow, the majority of London's' over-crowded dock and slum areas have either been cleared or re-developed and, whilst serious fires do regularly break out in London, they are rarely quite so great a threat to their surroundings.

As if to underline the constant hazards faced by its fire-fighters, another tragic and major fire took place in Glasgow in August 1972. Seven firemen, all wearing BA, were working inside a burning cash-and-carry warehouse when the roof collapsed and fell into the fiery interior. All seven men perished and, in a message of sympathy to relatives, Mr Gordon Campbell, the Secretary of State for Scotland, said: 'This is a tragic reminder of the debt we all owe to men of such heroism who perform a public service we can never take for granted.'

On the industrial-relations front, firemen over the years have slowly certainly achieved better pay and conditions, and a shorter working week of 48 hours. There was much negotiation over a satisfactory salary scale for the service generally, one to be fully commensurate with the skill and danger of a fireman's work. Most firemen would say that this rate has still not been achieved, and during negotiations of recent years there has been a certain air of confrontation between unions and local authority employers. In these days when so much emphasis is placed on industrial productivity, a fireman's work-load cannot be easily measured and assessed, though the soaring fire-loss statistics, and the terrible toll of human life and injuries at fires and other incidents, indicate his place in modern society.

Wrangling over firemen's pay came to a head in November 1977, when the first-ever national firemen's strike loomed. In the last few days before the strike, the British Fire Service was subjected to an overwhelming amount of TV, radio and press coverage, the like of which had been unknown in all its long history. Both sides of the dispute, the Fire Brigades Union and the local authorities, stood firm in their respective positions. Hundreds of 'green goddesses' – twenty-year old appliances – were prepared by soldiers, sailors and airmen up and down the country to provide some sort of fire cover through the strike that many firemen abhorred. Loyalties were divided as firemen had to face a decision between their consciences and the call of their union.

Once the strike had started, the public at large started to react to support their firemen. Signatures, pledges of support, and gifts of food and money came pouring in. Suddenly people seemed to be aware of what goes into the training of a fireman and what his life, albeit poorly paid, consists of. Banner headlines and graphic TV newsreels told of how the 'thin green line' of service men were coping with the emergency and attempting to contain the many small fires that soon became conflagrations. The servicemen, many of them young recruits, had a hopeless task for they were inadequately trained and poorly equipped. Most of their fire-fighting was from 'external' positions. Their courage and enthusiasm however was beyond question and, water damage apart, there can be little doubt that their efforts at many thousands of incidents in city, town and country over the nine weeks that the strike lasted saved countless properties from devastation by fire.

It was indeed a sad strike and one the Fire Service as a whole will long regret; for despite the undoubted value of the pay settlement that the strike achieved, the action itself pitched fireman against fireman and men against officers.

Perhaps the one obvious gain the strike brought to the Fire Service was the sheer amount of detailed coverage which the work of Fire Brigades received immediately before the dispute. It can only be hoped that this benefit will not be wholly dissipated by the strike's after-effects. Trade unionism has become tightly enmeshed in a life-saving service and some people involved with union organisation try to apply outside industrial parities to a fireman's job. I myself am one who believes that whilst the members of a public fire, rescue and emergency service do have rights that occasionally require improvement and defence, strikes do not belong to a fireman's job and never will.

This sorry period apart, the London Fire Brigade has come a long way over the years and the basic role of its firemen remains the same – to save life and to preserve property. In doing so, firemen often place themselves in grave danger. Since 1965, eleven London firemen have been killed in the course of duty and the next chapter is concerned with one such brave man that I personally knew, and the terrible fire at which he was tragically killed.

When the Roof Fell In

Fireman Hamish Harry Pettit came to my watch from training school in mid-1974, when as a Station Officer I had command of the Red Watch at Paddington Fire Station. Hamish was in his early twenties, enthusiastic and alert, and in his first few months had shown good practical sense, worked with great vigour at drills and was obviously keen to be 'a good fireman'. He had a quiet nature, settled into fire-station life very quickly and was well-liked by the rest of the watch. I was very satisfied with his progress when I filled in his mid-probation report, after Hamish had completed six months' service.

Then came the fateful night duty of Thursday 12th to Friday 13th December 1974.

The shift started as usual at 6pm, when after roll-call and appliance checks, my Sub-Officer was able to take a refresher session on knots and lines. For two hours the call-out bells were silent, which for Paddington was unusual. Soon after roll-call Hamish had been to an interview with the Divisional Officer, who had confirmed Hamish's satisfactory probationary progress. Then at 8pm, still as yet undisturbed, the watch went to supper. For a station that answered over 3,500 emergency calls a year this was too good to last.

Just as I sat down to fish-and-chips with the twenty-one Red Watch firemen in the first-floor mess, the call-out bells rang. Groans mingled with the noise of firemen jostling for position as they made their way out into the corridor and down the two poles to the four waiting appliances below.

This first call of the shift was for the TL only, to a fire in a launderette on Willesden's area. The TL and its crew roared off into the night with blue lights flashing. The remainder of us made our way back to the deserted mess to collect the abandoned plates and as the TL crew's meals were put into the hotplate, the call-out bells clanged out again. 'ET' read the appliance indicator lights and it was quickly moving off to a road accident involving a lorry on Hammersmith's area. The pattern for the night was set. During the next six hours, there were four more calls for Paddington's appliances.

Hamish Pettit was crewing the PE and happy with himself following the complimentary remarks made to him earlier in the evening. Around 2.30am, he and the rest of Red Watch tried to settle down after the disturbance of the sixth 'shout' – for the ET only – and the lights in the firemen's dormitory were turned off yet again.

All calls had so far been to a motley assortment of minor jobs: small fires in a shop-front neon sign and in a street excavation, persons 'shut in lift', shattered glazing caused by a falling window-box – just a routine night. At 3.30am the automatic lighting throughout the station flashed on once more and call bells assaulted drowsy minds. 'Fire – The Worsley Hotel, Clifton Gardens, W9' read the cryptic teleprinter slip. This address was only half a mile from Paddington Fire Station and all four appliances were ordered by Wembley Control. As I struggled into my boots and leggings, I sensed this was going to be a working job; I could already smell acrid smoke. Then as the electrically operated appliance-room doors opened, I saw clouds of drifting smoke being carried along by the wind, so thick that they spasmodically dimmed the amber street-lights outside the fire station.

Within a minute of the call, all four appliances were noisily on their way over the short distance to the hotel. One by one, they were totally enveloped in the smoke until a minute later they each swung into Clifton Gardens, upwind and in front of the Worsley.

As I jumped down from the P, a serious fire was already involving several upper floors of the large five-storey hotel and as the billowing smoke momentarily parted, I could see to my horror that over thirty people were clinging perilously to ledges, hanging out of windows and gathering on one end of the roof. Many more occupants of the hotel were fleeing the burning and smoking building. Everywhere was pandemonium. Naked and pyjama-clad people milled around in panic in the street. Those trapped above by the fire screamed out to me and my crews for rescue.

The Red Watch leapt into action but I already feared that, for some, rescue would be too late. Several people out on ledges looked ready to jump, for fire was breaking out fiercely through more windows along the frontage of the hotel and thick rolling smoke poured out of those not yet showing orange flame.

Wheeled escapes crashed off PE's and were manhandled into position despite many awkwardly parked cars in the hotel service road. Hook ladders were heaved off appliances and the first jets of water trained on the frontage of the hotel to cool the first firemen from the intense radiated heat as they ascended the escape ladders to the trapped persons. One dramatic rescue followed another, as firemen coaxed and cajoled the imperilled and frightened groups onto their ladders and down to safety.

More and more appliances began to arrive in response to my urgent radio requests to Control for more assistance. Many rescues were also carried out at the rear of the hotel, under the most extreme conditions. Crews faced intense heat, billowing smoke and showers of sparks to get up to people crying out for help. In some of this work Hamish was actively involved.

Once all the visible rescues had been successfully completed before anyone jumped, the battle to contain the spreading fire began in earnest. Firemen on all sides worked slowly together

(*Opposite*)
Rescue of firemen by firemen. A 30 pump fire at the Worsley Hotel, Maida Vale, London W9, 13 December 1974. After $1\frac{1}{4}$ hours of digging, Fireman Tony Stewart is lifted out of the burning debris in which he has been buried. Note the severe scorch marks across the hotel frontage and the two turntable ladders ready overhead should they be needed (*LFB*)

to surround the thunderous, roaring inferno that had now broken out through the roof of the hotel. Inside the building two stone staircases had collapsed very early on, and crews rigged in BA penetrating that part of the hotel with jets had first to rig ladders over the gaping voids to pursue the fiery mass funnelling up the stair-well above. As well as present danger and discomfort, the firemen had to contend with a rapidly worsening fire situation involving remote parts of the building, as fire spread along corridors, up the lift-shaft and staircases to the floors above.

After about an hour, as crews from many fire stations worked off ladders and up staircases to the heart of the fire, part of the hotel roof suddenly collapsed. The fire-weakened structure crashed into the room below and this floor, also weak through fire damage to the joists, gave way, and the entire smoking flaming mass fell into Room 13 on the second floor, burying a Station Officer and three firemen who were working a jet there.

At first, when the nearest firemen to the collapse, including myself, scrambled up a ladder to the window of the smoking room, only two of the trapped crew were visible. Both were conscious but in obvious pain and buried chest-high by the fall. The whereabouts of the third fireman was soon discovered amid the piled and smoking debris when he waved his hand out of the impacted timbers. He was almost totally buried. All three were in danger of being slowly roasted alive from the burning fires in the wreckage in which they were trapped. Rescue teams quickly set to work, and dug with their bare hands at the hot bricks and massive wooden beams. Indeed, firemen were now faced with a rescue of a different sort – fireman dug for fireman, friend for friend, mate for mate. To add to the hazards within the tiny room, choking smoke and steam made it almost impossible at times for the rescue teams to see what they were doing, and frequent falls from dislodged brickwork and still-burning timbers overhead added urgency to the operation.

Following one and a half hours of sheer dogged determination by the rescue teams in the most awful conditions in that small room, the first two trapped firemen were extricated, brought down to street level and rushed to hospital, both badly burned and injured. The rescue of the third fireman was a more difficult task because of the sheer weight of debris upon him. Sadly, as his rescuers toiled, swore, coughed and spluttered amid the swirling gloom, they discovered the lifeless form of another fireman buried even deeper. This was young Hamish. When he was extricated from the collapse some time after, the last of the four-man crew to be freed, he was certified dead on the spot by a doctor from a medical team who had come to the building soon after the collapse. He had suffocated to death.

Two of the three survivors of the collapse came from my watch and one of these, like Hamish, was a recent recruit to the Brigade. The other was an experienced fireman of over twelve years' service. The world had indeed fallen in also on me and the rest of my watch. Along with those of my men that I could find, I walked away from the still-smouldering, evil-looking, blackened hotel. The dawn had broken across the morning sky and we had been at the fire for almost five hours. As I looked around and tried hard to restrain my tears, I noticed some of my Trojan fire-fighters had clean streaks running down their grubby, smoke-stained faces, tears of men not normally given to such displays of emotion.

Out of a magnificent and successful rescue situation in the early stages of the fire had come tragedy, death and suffering to firemen themselves. Despite the rescues of over thirty persons in the first few minutes of our arrival, clearing-up crews later discovered the charred remains of six residents. Later still, we were to discover that the cause of the fire was arson.

Once back at the fire station, the awful reality of what had happened slowly penetrated our exhausted minds and bodies. It became increasingly difficult to contain ourselves. Grief was on everyone's face and an unusually subdued air hung over the station. After a brief and warming shower, the watch gathered in the mess and listened to the morning radio reports of the hotel fire. We supped cups of strong tea, unable to face breakfast.

As the incoming day watch began to arrive I put my soaking and smoke-pungent fire-gear away in the uniform room. I didn't envy the carriers of the sad news to Hamish's next-of-kin. Divisional Officer Clisby from Headquarters was already being rushed down to Rochester, Kent, to break the news to his widow. Charles Clisby had performed this thankless duty on several such occasions in the past. In fact in February 1974, Red Watch personnel at Paddington Fire Station had been chosen to illustrate a thirty-minute TV film about Clisby's fire-service poetry; part of this film included a short piece entitled 'Breaking the News', in which Clisby relates just what it is like to have to confront a wife with her husband's death in the line of duty. One line of this work reads: 'The roof fell in'.

Breaking the News

I spoke as calmly as I could,
'Do please sit down, I've brought your Mum,'
At this the girl then understood.

'Oh No!' she cried, 'Oh God! Oh God!'
Picked up their infant from its cot.
'He's dead,' she said. I simply nod.

'By how? A fire?' I nod again.
Her thoughts are for the little one.
'The roof fell in. He felt no pain.'

The fewest words, two moves of head.
My task is done. Hers has begun.
The going's hard. Tears will be shed.

Charles Clisby

As I prepared myself in the station office for the many tasks and phone calls which would come during that dreadful morning, I realised the bitter irony of the tragedy of Friday 13th. In making the TV film, and with the choice of 342 individual watches at London fire stations, Clisby had chosen

the very watch at Paddington that was itself to suffer death
and injury only ten months later. As expected the station
telephones rang continuously as many anxious female voices
asked if their man was safe, and there were many highly
emotional moments during these calls. I answered several
calls from distraught off-duty members of the watch who had
heard of the death of a fireman and injuries to three others at
the Worsley fire on the news bulletins. Hamish's name was
not released to the media until his wife had been informed,
and it was my sad duty to inform those Red Watch callers of
who had been killed and injured.

Another of my priorities that morning was to visit St Mary's
Hospital in Praed Street where the injured had been taken.
When I arrived they had not long been transferred to a ward
from casualty, and I was amongst their first official visitors.
I was allowed to briefly see all three of them, alongside one
another in adjacent beds. Each had drips set up and some of
their burns were still exposed. Their eyes were those of men
who had been to hell and back yet weak smiles bore evidence
of unbroken spirit. During my quiet talk with each of them I
confirmed the death of Hamish in the roof collapse and each
man in turn wept quite openly. As I was leaving, their shocked
wives were just arriving outside the ward, having been
collected by official Brigade cars from their homes.

Before I drove back to Paddington fire station, I sat in my
parked car to settle my heavy emotions. Hamish was dead and
three others were all badly burned. All four had been carrying
out the basic functions of a fireman – rescue of trapped persons
and the preservation of property – and, in doing so, Hamish
had made the ultimate sacrifice.

Then I thought ahead to the probable full Brigade funeral,
when hundreds of uniformed firemen from London and other
Brigades all over the country would line up to pay their final
respects to Hamish Pettit. I knew full well that as Hamish's
Station Officer I would be intimately involved in this and
recalled the occasion in 1969 when I attended the funeral of
five London firemen killed in an East End oil-tank explosion.

At this time I was a Leading Fireman, one of many fire-fighters lined up at attention along the long narrow path to Stratford parish church. The cortège with its five coffins, draped in Union Jacks and with firemen pall-bearers, had paused at the entrance to the church. Directly in front of my position in the guard-of-honour was the first of the coffins and behind it stood the dead firemen's Station Officer. He had tears rolling down his cheeks: how I had felt for that suffering man those five years ago.

I started my car and drove slowly along Praed Street, past the glittering decorations in the shops. It was only two weeks to Christmas. As I halted at traffic-lights at the Edgware Road, my eyes caught a newspaper seller's placard which proclaimed 'Fireman hero dies in London hotel blaze', and my mind drifted back to the horrors of the protracted rescues of the trapped men at the Worsley Hotel during the cold and dark hours before dawn.

Back at Paddington fire station, I saw that the pile of gear and equipment brought back from the hotel fire had mounted up in the drill yard. Throughout the remainder of the day duty, the Blue Watch were frequently disturbed in their cleaning and testing work by 'shouts' as the call bells sounded out again and again. There were many matters to attend to before my watch paraded for their second night duty. My Divisional Officer was ready to initiate arrangements for a full Brigade funeral should Hamish's widow so desire and I wanted to be *au fait* with procedures. Several newspaper reporters wanted to ask about the various aspects of the Worsley fire and the rescues of the firemen. There was also a sadder, more personal task to perform – to check, list and empty the contents of Hamish's locker. It was late afternoon when I stood alone in the spacious empty dormitory on the first floor and turned the locker key. Inside its door I was confronted with a small photograph of a little boy, stuck on with strips of Sellotape. This was Hamish's only child, one and a half years old, smiling and being carried aloft by his father on some previous happy occasion.

This job over, I prepared for parade and roll-call. At 6pm, six bells rang throughout the fire station to signify 'change of watch' and the Red Watch fell in in two single files against the four red appliances whose cab doors were open awaiting the first call of the night shift. The watch stood motionless and silent in their full fire-uniforms and I nodded to my Sub-Officer alongside me. He held the watch roll-call board upon which there was now a conspicuous space in the alphabetical list of names, and he smartly called the watch to attention.

As I proudly surveyed the two rows of firemen, I saw that tears had started to fall yet again for Hamish and his loss.

Epilogue

Massey Shaw's rigidly disciplined fire-fighters of the last century are the predecessors of the London firemen of today. There have been many changes in the Brigade over the last hundred years, not least of which is that discipline in the Brigade nowadays is far less exacting than of old, although every firemen in the UK is still subject to a discipline code. If breaking it is proven against a man, punishment varying from stoppage of pay to dismissal can be awarded. The average age of today's firemen is younger then ever before – in London around the early twenties – and many of these young men are well qualified academically. Some have forsaken better-paid careers in the outside world to join the Fire Brigade, perhaps leaving the boredom and frustrations of commercial life for a world where initiative, resourcefulness and a sense of purpose are better employed. It must be clearly stated, however, that brains alone never put out fires. I recall an instructor at training school saying that to be a success in the Brigade one needed the physical strength of a navvy together with a handful of degrees in science and engineering.

By the very nature of his work, a fireman must be a jack-of-all-trades, understand a little about a lot. Hydraulics, chemistry, physics, first-aid, building construction, are all needed in order to cope with the situations that confront him. He must have a head for working at heights, be able to endure extremes of temperature by day or night, and keep himself physically fit. And sometimes, in the early morning in a dwelling in some

London street, he may have to administer last rites over a body in which life is obviously extinct.

Every day and night throughout the year, the on-duty watches at fire stations throughout Greater London are ready to respond to whatever act of human misfortune, folly or accident demands and taxes their skills and equipment. A watch is in fact rather like a large closely knit family, where a fireman is a part of a well-drilled team machine, yet must still be able to act and think for himself in emergency situations, where seconds can mean death to a trapped and suffering person. An individual fireman is also well aware that somewhere, someday, his own life may depend on his fellows' action and rapid response in positions of great danger.

Working on a watch you learn a lot from your fellows; to understand their foibles and to laugh at yourself. Indeed, I have often heard the view that going on duty is less like going to work than like entering a rather exclusive masculine club. The atmosphere of a well-run fire station, the sense of belonging to a team that the public look to in times of crisis, all help to engender this feeling – one which is widely felt by firemen throughout the British Fire Service. One works, trains and relaxes in the company of fine men, some of whom have been decorated for their bravery at various incidents, both large and small, over the years. On-duty time is rarely dull, and when the bells 'go down' in a fire station the whole watch comes together in experience and ability as it turns out to another emergency.

In this computer age there will always be a role for firemen. No matter how sophisticated automatic fire-detection and protection systems become, there can never be a substitute for the intensely physical work of a fireman. His service is the nation's major emergency and rescue organisation.

For me, being a professional firemen is a fascinating and totally absorbing way of life, for there is real satisfaction in preparing for and helping the public at large in their time of need. There have, though, been occasions when deep inside a burning building I have been very scared. In the dense smoke and humid heat, I could have been lost in a maze rather than be one of a BA crew working a jet along a basement corridor, searching for the seat of the outbreak perhaps somewhere nearby. But working in the close company of a well-trained team, I learnt the self-discipline that all firemen must acquire in the face of danger. Indeed, by the very action of entering a smoking building from which all others are fleeing, firemen surely display a special brand of courage. A Brigade friend of mine, Colin Searl, summed this up so very succinctly. He was one of those three firemen trapped in the Worsley Hotel blaze collapse described in the previous chapter, and he suffered uncomplainingly for one and a half hours before he was finally dug out. Before he could be released, his right buttock and leg were both badly burned in the hot debris all around him; such was the extent of his injury that he had a long stay in the famous McIndoe burns unit at East Grinstead in Sussex, where he underwent extensive skin grafting.

For weeks Colin lay in appalling pain. I visited him regularly during the long weeks of his stay at East Grinstead, and in the days of Christmas 1974 he just could not lie in a settled position for longer than a minute, such was the searing pain from his multiple burns. It was agonising to watch his suffering from the bedside. Then he contracted pleurisy, and, on one New Year's visit looked as if he was dying. But with excellent nursing care, he fought back and very slowly over the weeks grew stronger. The surgeon feared that he would never walk properly again, but he showed a single-minded determination to regain the use of his leg and get back on duty as soon as possible.

Once he was finally discharged, Colin took to riding his bicycle every day, for he was a cycling fan. He continued with rigorous exercises to regain the use of the leg, but all down the upper part of the limb he was still appallingly scarred. He eventually returned to full fire-fighting duties in June 1975, some six months after the fatal collapse at the Worsley, and was soon in action again, leading a crew of firemen into a major London fire involving the upper floors of a men's hostel.

Afterwards, a reporter asked him how he felt when he first went into this fire after his long and enforced lay-off. He replied that he had a terrible feeling that the roof was going to collapse and that he'd never felt like that before. He never thought anything would happen to him. He'd heard a child say to a fireman one day: 'You are brave, mister,' and that made the job worthwhile. 'But we aren't brave – Massey Shaw said a fireman must enter buildings, from below, above and from every side. He said to be successful a fireman must get in and stay in. We know our job. It's part of our tradition. We are professionals.'

Throughout my own service I have seen a tremendous amount of life in the varied community that firemen everywhere exist to serve, just as my first Station Officer said I would. I too have learnt to be a little of a builder, engineer, electrician, chemist, doctor and psychologist. Perhaps one day Utopia will arrive and people will be more careful with lighted cigarette-ends, remove television plugs from sockets and use more respect with paraffin heaters, gas cylinders and blow-lamps. Perhaps children will no longer play with matches. A fireman's role may then be a preventive and educational one; but sadly I doubt it. The London Fire Brigade answered 55,516 urgent 999 calls in 1966, of which over 30,000 were actual fires. Ten years later, for exactly the same Brigade area, the total number of calls was 111,520, and of these over 63,000 were fire incidents. Fire losses continue to soar into hundreds of millions pounds each year. Firemen look set for busy times ahead.

Even as I write the final paragraphs of this book, I can hear the intermittent two-tone horns and fire-bells as several appliances from nearby Paddington Fire Station turn out to another 999 call. Fire-fighting, like many other pursuits in life, gets into one's blood; and as the raucous and discordant tones fade into the near distance, I am mentally with the fire-crews on board. I wonder what they are going to; it may only be a small rubbish fire in the open air, or it could be a drowsy smoker who has dropped a lighted cigarette-end down the back of a sofa. They may be rushing to a fire that has already smouldered neglected in an office or factory for some hours after closing time and has now gathered enough strength to burst angrily through the roof in a fiery glow for all to see. Even worse, their call may be to a smoke-choked labyrinth of an extensive sub-basement; no one outside in the street watching the pungent dark smoke pouring out of the building will be able to assist the firemen and tell them exactly what is burning or just where in the passageways deep under the street the fire is located. The crews will don breathing-apparatus and head into the smoke, totally blind, to seek the enemy at close quarters. Quite possibly, the appliances may be heading for a bloody road accident, or to a chemical tanker on its side, spewing out a deadly cargo. Their destination may be to a frustrating malicious false alarm.

The sound of the two-tone horns has faded now and finally stopped. Firemen from Paddington have arrived at the scene of the emergency. I wonder how they are getting on.

Neil Wallington
Maida Vale, London
October 1978

Bibliography

Ballantyne, R. M., *Fighting the Flames*, Thomas Nelson & Sons, 1867

Fire, April/August 1960

Fireman, January 1883

HMSO, *Report of the Cunningham Inquiry into the work of the Fire Service*, Cmnd 4807, November 1971

Holloway, Sally, *London's Noble Fire Brigades 1833–1904*, Cassell, 1973

Honeycombe, Gordon, *Red Watch*, Hutchinson, 1976

Jackson, W. Eric, *London's Fire Brigades*, Longmans, 1966

Massey Shaw, Eyre, *A Complete Manual on the Organisation, Machinery, Discipline and General Working of the Fire Brigade of London*, C. & E. Layton, 1876

Acknowledgements

I gratefully acknowledge the help of many firemen friends and colleagues with whom I have served at various fire stations of the London Brigade over the past years, and who have jogged my memory on certain of the happenings related.

I also wish to acknowledge use of short extracts from the fire-Service poetry of the late Charles Clisby. And I thank Jim O'Sullivan of the London Fire Brigade Library; the staff of the Brigade's photographic section; Gordon White, LFB Press Officer; Owen Rowland for the use of some of his photographs, and Adrian Falks for processing most of the prints used in illustration.

The encouragement given to me by Gordon Honeycombe during the undertaking of this work and the Foreword he has contributed are greatly appreciated.

Lastly, I wish to point out that any opinions expressed in these pages on Fire Service matters are entirely my own.

Neil Wallington

Index